SPORTS QUIZZES

THE QUIZ BOOK COMPANY

First published in 2004 by
The Quiz Book Company Ltd
Bardfield Centre,
Great Bardfield, Essex, CM7 4SL

ISBN 1-84236-509-6

Printed in India

Some of the material in this book has been used
previously in The Great Big Quiz Book.
Other questions written by Chris Rigby.

QUIZ 1

. . . .

1 What is the name of the kick in Rugby Union which follows a try?

2 Which boxer married actress Robbin Givens?

3 'Party Politics' won the Grand National in what year?

4 Who is the only footballer ever to play in three World Cup winning teams?

5 How many triple word score squares are there on a Scrabble board?

6 In what sport do you play for the Pilkington Cup?

7 With which sport do you associate Roberto Duran?

8 What football club does well known BBC Sports presenter Des Lynam support?

9 From what country does racing driver Jacques Villeneuve come?

10 How many dice do you use in the popular game Yahtzee?

ANSWERS

1. Conversion. 2. Mike Tyson. 3. 1992. 4. Pele. 5. Eight. 6. Rugby Union.
7. Boxing. 8. Brighton and Hove Albion. 9. Canada. 10. Five dice.

QUIZ 2

• •

1 In which sport does the pitcher stand on a mound in the middle of a diamond?

2 White, yellow, orange, green, blue, brown. What comes next?

3 The national championships of which sport are held at Hurlingham?

4 Which country hosted the 1998 Commonwealth Games?

5 What nationality connects the snooker world champions Ray Reardon, Mark Williams and Terry Griffiths?

6 In bullfighting, what is an estoque?

7 In which sport did Karen Smithies gain international recognition for England?

8 Which famous trophy was stolen from a Birmingham shop window in 1895?

9 In which sport is the winning team required to travel a distance of 3.6m?

10 In which Olympic event are competitors required to wear a top hat?

ANSWERS

1. Baseball 2. Black, grades of judo belts 3. Croquet 4. Malaysia 5. Welsh 6. Sword 7. Cricket 8. FA Cup 9. Tug of war 10. Dressage

QUIZ 3

• •

Identify the cricket counties from their initials letters
and nicknames

1   W   Bears

2   G   Gladiators

3   D   Scorpions

4   N   Outlaws

5   M   Crusaders

6   N   Steelbacks

7   W   Royals

8   H   Hawks

9   L   Lightning

10 S   Sabres

ANSWERS

1. Warwickshire 2. Gloucestershire 3. Derbyshire 4. Nottinghamshire
5. Middlesex 6. Northamptonshire 7. Worcestershire 8. Hampshire
9. Lancashire 10. Somerset

QUIZ 4

- -

1　What is the nickname of Swansea City FC?

2　Which celebrity chef sits on the board of Norwich City FC?

3　What is the retirement age for Premiership referees?

4　Who was named the Goalkeeper of the Tournament for the 2002 World Cup?

5　Which British city plays host to the Old Firm derby?

6　Who was the first Dutch footballer to be voted European Footballer of the Year?

7　Which club side have former England managers Alf Ramsey and Bobby Robson both managed?

8　Which World Cup winner of 1966 was later granted honorary citizenship of Ireland?

9　What is the alternative name of West Ham's home ground The Boleyn Ground?

10　Who was appointed as manager of Scotland's national team in February 2002?

ANSWERS

1. The Swans 2. Delia Smith 3. 48 4. Oliver Kahn 5. Glasgow 6. Johann Cruyff 7. Ipswich Town 8. Jack Charlton 9. Upton Park 10. Bertie Vogts

QUIZ 5

1. How many points does a cannon score in billiards?

2. What is the first discipline contested in a triathlon event?

3. In what type of race is the Little Brown Jug contested in the USA?

4. Which European nation lifted tennis's Davis Cup in 1997 and 1998?

5. At which sport was Eddie Waring a famous commentator?

6. What do the initials GS signify on a netball bib?

7. What is the longest distance for a running event in a decathlon?

8. What sport is played by the Brisbane Lions?

9. In which sport is a Christmas Tree starting line used?

10. For which Formula One team did Ralf Schumacher in the 2004 season?

ANSWERS

1. 2 points 2. Swimming 3. Harness racing 4. Sweden 5. Rugby League
6. Goal shoot 7. 1500 metres 8. Australian rules football 9. Drag racing
10. Williams

QUIZ 6

• •

All ten answers begin with the letter A

1 What was originally called the 100 Guineas Cup?

2 Which club won soccer's European Champions Cup in 1982?

3 What was the French venue for the 1992 Winter Olympics?

4 In golf what name is given to the short cut grass between the fairway and the approach to the green?

5 Which American football team are known as The Braves?

6 Who owned the Epsom Derby winner, Sinndar?

7 Which Scottish football club are nicknamed, The Wee Rovers?

8 Which AA was crowned Wimbledon champion in 1975?

9 Which city in the southern hemisphere hosted the Commonwealth Games in 1990?

10 Which horse was first past the post in the 1981 Grand National?

ANSWERS

1. America's Cup 2. Aston Villa 3. Albertville 4. Apron 5. Atlanta 6. Aga Khan 7. Albion Rovers 8. Arthur Ashe 9. Aukland 10. Aldaniti

QUIZ 7

• •

1   In which city is the Sabina Park cricket stadium?

2   Which England international cricket star was killed in a car crash in March 2002?

3   How many runs comprise a double Nelson?

4   Which cricket almanac has been published annually since 1864?

5   In what year were the Ashes known as Botham's Ashes?

6   Which England cricket star recorded his 100th Test century in 1977?

7   Which Australian cricket legend ended his career with a Test batting average of 99.94?

8   Which is the only Welsh county that boasts a first class county cricket team?

9   What does the W stand for in the name of WG Grace?

10 In 1968, who became the first batsman to score six 6's off one over?

ANSWERS

1. Kingston, Jamaica 2. Ben Hollioake 3. 222 4. Wisden's Almanac 5. 1981
6. Geoff Boycott 7. Sir Donald Bradman 8. Glamorgan 9. William 10. Gary
Sobers

QUIZ 8

1 In which county is Sandown Park race course?

2 Founded in 1908, what dot he initials IIHF stand for?

3 In the world of sport did Jack Broughton invent the golf tee, boxing gloves or shin pads?

4 What name is given to a racehorse that has not yet won a race?

5 In 2003, who became the youngest British footballer to win 50 international caps?

6 Which European nation shocked the yachting world in 2003 by winning the America's Cup?

7 What was the previous name of the Commonwealth Games?

8 What do the initials TO stand for with regard to a cricket dismissal?

9 Which football ground houses the Scottish Football Museum?

10 Which country were represented in the Commonwealth Games by the initials RSA?

ANSWERS

1. Surrey 2. International Ice Hockey Federation 3. Boxing gloves 4. Maiden
5. Michael Owen 6. Switzerland 7. The Empire Games 8. Timed out
9. Hampden Park 10. South Africa

QUIZ 9

All ten answers begin with the letter B

1 Which football club plays its home matches at Gigg Lane?

2 In the world of sport what is 13.4 metres long and 6.1 metres wide?

3 What B is a score of one over par for a hole in golf?

4 Which sport featured in the Gene Hackman movie Best Shot?

5 What B is the name given to a barbed stick in bullfighting?

6 In the Olympic games, in which sport is the Val Barker Trophy awarded?

7 For which swimming stroke did Duncan Goodhew win an Olympic gold medal?

8 In snooker, on which line are the yellow, green and brown balls placed at the start of play?

9 What is the name of the trophy presented to the winners of the Indianapolis 500?

10 In 1839, what was named on Aintree race course after one of the jockeys?

ANSWERS

1. Bury 2. Badminton court 3. Bogey 4. Basketball 5. Banderilla 6. Boxing
7. Breaststroke 8. Baulk line 9. Borg Warner Trophy 10. Becher's Brook

QUIZ 10

• •

1 What R is the name given to a series of yachting races?

2 In which sport are the goalkeepers the only players that are allowed to stand on the floor?

3 K1 and K2 are both categories in which Olympic event?

4 Which Scottish swimmer collected an Olympic gold medal at the 1976 games?

5 Which sport is governed by the IWSF?

6 Which politician competed in the Admiral's Cup in a yacht called Morning Cloud?

7 In the 1912 university boat race did the Oxford crew, the Cambridge crew or both crews sink?

8 At what height are springboard diving events in the Olympics contested?

9 In which sport might competitors suffer a wipe out whilst attempting to perform a tube ride?

10 In which sport is the Harmsworth Cup contested?

ANSWERS

1. Regatta 2. Water polo 3. Canoeing or kayaking 4. David Wilkie 5. Water skiing 6. Edward Heath 7. Both crews 8. 3 metres 9. Surfing 10. Powerboat racing

QUIZ 11

• •

1 Which letter of the Greek alphabet is also the name of a leading sports goods company?

2 What sport is played by a team called Manchester Storm?

3 The winners of which annual sporting event are presented with the Vince Lombardi Trophy?

4 Which Scottish born snooker star won the world title in 1998?

5 What sport is played by the Brooklyn Dodgers?

6 Which venue hosted the first ever Olympic Games in 776 BC?

7 Which electronics company did Vodafone replace as the shirt sponsors of Manchester United?

8 Which sport featured in the film When We Were Kings?

9 At which club did Frank Clark replace Brian Clough as manager?

10 Is the penholder grip used in table tennis, bowls or judo?

ANSWERS

1. Kappa 2. Ice hockey 3. The Superbowl 4. John Higgins 5. Baseball
6. Olympia 7. Sharp 8. Boxing 9. Nottingham Forest 10. Table tennis

QUIZ 12

• •

All ten answers begin with the letter C

1. Which football nation were crowned African Nations Champions in 2002?

2. What nine-letter C word is the name given to a twin hulled yacht or boat?

3. Miguel Indurain is a famous name in which sport?

4. In which event did Formula One star Jackie Stewart represent Great Britian in the Olympics?

5. Which was the only non English club to win the FA Cup in the 20th century?

6. What five-letter C word is the name given to the stick used in shinty?

7. Which country hosted the 1976 Olympic games?

8. In the world of sport what has a maximum width of 10.8cm?

9. What are snooker balls made from?

10. Which horse race completes the Autumn Double with the Cambridgeshire?

ANSWERS

1. Cameroon 2. Catamaran 3. Cycling 4. Clay pigeon shooting 5. Cardiff City 6. Caman 7. Canada 8. Cricket bat 9. Crystallate 10. Cesarewitch

QUIZ 13

1 In what year was Muhammed Ali stripped of his world title for refusing the Vietnam War draft?

2 What is the last name of the boxer Prince Naseem?

3 What boxing weight category comes between light-heavyweight and heavyweight?

4 What do the initials WBU stand for?

5 Who, born Walker Smith, went on to become a world champion boxer?

6 Which British boxer did Mike Tyson defeat in five rounds in 1989?

7 What nickname was used by the heavyweight boxer James Smith?

8 Was Sonny Liston's first name Cedric, Christopher or Charles?

9 Which boxing weight category has an upper weight limit of 67 kg?

10 For which nation did Lennox Lewis secure an Olympic gold medal?

ANSWERS

1. 1967 2. Hamed 3. Cruiserweight 4. World Boxing Union 5. Sugar Ray Robinson 6. Frank Bruno 7. Bonecrusher 8. Charles 9. Welterweight 10. Canada

QUIZ 14

. . . .

1 What is known as the sport of kings?

2 In which decade was the first London marathon contested?

3 What was the nationality of the man who instigated the modern Olympics?

4 What is the name of the home ground of Sheffield Wednesday FC?

5 In which city is Candlestick Park baseball stadium?

6 Which sporting contest was first won in 1976 when the Green Bay Packers beat the Kansas City Chiefs?

7 Which Yorkshire town is the home town of cricket umpire Dickie Bird?

8 What bird provides the nickname of Cardiff City FC?

9 Which town links the birthplace of Muhammed Ali and the venue of the Kentucky Derby?

10 What flower features on the badge of Blackburn Rovers FC?

ANSWERS

1. Horse racing 2. 1980's , 1981 3. French, Baron Pierre de Coubterin
4. Hillsborough 5. San Francisco 6. The Superbowl 7. Barnsley 8. Bluebird
9. Louisville 10. Red rose

QUIZ 15

. . . .

All ten answers begin with the letter D

1   In which sport was John Part crowned world champion in 2003?

2   What name is given to the playing area in a game of baseball?

3   Which sporting event derives its name from the Greek words for ten and contest?

4   Which football country were the surprise winners of the 1992 European Nations Championships?

5   In which sport is Greg Louganis a past Olympic champion?

6   Which was the first football club to win the Scottish League championship?

7   In golf, what canine name is given to a hole that bends to one side?

8   Which town is home to the Formula One racing circuit at Magny Cours?

9   Which trophy did Spain win in 2000 by defeating Australia 3-1 in the final?

10 With which football club did Brian Clough win his first league title?

ANSWERS

1. Darts 2. Diamond 3. Decathlon 4. Denmark 5. Diving 6. Dumbarton
7. Dog leg 8. Dijon 9. Davis Cup 10. Derby County

QUIZ 16

• •

1 In which country did the martial art of Tai Chi originate?

2 What takes place in a ring called a dojo?

3 In which sport is a white uniform called a gi worn?

4 What W is the term given to a half point in judo?

5 Which combat sport is divided into the three categories of light contact, semi contact and full contact?

6 Tiger, dragon and snake are all styles of what?

7 What has a name that means, way of the sword?

8 What nickname was given to the boxer Joe Walcott?

9 What number of Dan represents the highest grade in judo?

10 What sport is divided into the three categories of above waist, whole body and metallic jacket only?

ANSWERS

1. China 2. Sumo wrestling 3. Karate 4. Wazari 5. Kick boxing 6. Kung fu
7. Kendo 8. Jersey Joe 9. 12th dan 10. Fencing

QUIZ 17

1. FITA is the governing body of which sport?

2. In which sport was the Victorian Football League founded in 1877?

3. What bird features on the badge of Tottenham Hotspur FC?

4. Who won the Six Nations rugby union championships in 2002?

5. Which golfer was nicknamed Supermex despite being born in Texas?

6. Which sport's hall of fame was founded in Cooperstown in 1936?

7. What does a red flag signify in Formula One motor racing?

8. In which country did bobsleigh racing originate in the 19th century?

9. What do the initials RO stand for with regard to a cricket dismissal?

10. Which country does Australia play cricket against when contesting the Worrell Trophy?

ANSWERS

1. Archery 2. Australian rules football 3. Cockerel 4. France 5. Lee Trevino
6. Baseball 7. Premature end of a race 8. Switzerland 9. Run out 10. West
Indies

QUIZ 18

All ten answers begin with the letter E

1 What E is a type of sword used in fencing?

2 Which German side did Real Madrid defeat 7-3 to win the 1960 European Cup?

3 Which golf trophy, instigated in 1958, was named after the serving US President?

4 Which horse was first past the post in the abandoned 1993 Grand National?

5 What is the name of the home ground of Leeds United FC?

6 Who won the Ladies Singles title at Wimbledon in 1980?

7 Who became a boxing world champion when he knocked out Buster Douglas in 1990?

8 In the 1956 Melbourne Olympics, which events were held in Stockholm due to quarantine laws?

9 Which Wigan rugby star received the Man of Steel Award in 1989?

10 What call is made by a fencer to inform an opponent to adopt a defensive stance?

ANSWERS

1. Epee 2. Eintracht Frankfurt 3. Eisenhower Trophy 4. Esha Ness 5. Elland Road 6. Evonne Cawley 7. Evander Holyfield 8. Equestrian events 9. Ellery Hanley 10. En garde

QUIZ 19

1 Which footballer scored for both sides in the 1981 FA Cup final?

2 The London underground station, Gillespie Rd, was renamed in the 1930s after which football club?

3 Which Italian club plays its home matches at the Stadio Delle Alpi?

4 Which is the only English football league club that has a name ending with the letter G?

5 In what year did Brazil win their first World Cup?

6 In 1966, who became the first footballer to be voted BBC Sports Personality Of The Year?

7 What is the nationality of the football star Jimmy Floyd Hasselbaink?

8 Which Scottish football club are nicknamed The Bhoys?

9 Which English football club are nicknamed, The Seasiders?

10 Which Spanish city is home to Real Betis FC?

ANSWERS

1. Tommy Hutchinson 2. Arsenal 3. Juventus 4. Reading 5. 1958 6. Bobby Moore 7. Dutch 8. Celtic 9. Blackpool 10. Seville

QUIZ 20

• •

1 Which nation won the greatest number of gold medals at the 2000 Sydney Olympics?

2 Who captained Liverpool to FA Cup glory in 2001?

3 In which sport does the height of the net stand at 15.25 cm?

4 Sepong is the venue for which country's Formula One Grand Prix?

5 In yachting, what is a spinnaker?

6 What do the initials GRA signify with regard to a sporting body?

7 In which sport might a competitior be given a mandatory eight count?

8 Which golfer carried the Olympic torch across the Sydney Harbour Bridge in 2000?

9 What is a cricket umpire signalling when extending one arm horizontally?

10 What is a cricket umpire signalline when extending both arms horizontally?

ANSWERS

1. USA 2. Sami Hypia 3. Table tennis 4. Malaysia 5. A sail 6. Greyhound Racing Association 7. Boxing 8. Greg Norman 9. No ball 10. A wide

QUIZ 21

All ten answers begin with the letter F

1. What is the ice hockey equivalent of a kick off called?

2. In which weight category did Barry McGuigan become a boxing world champion?

3. Which governing body in soccer was founded in 1904?

4. Who was named BBC Sports Personality Of The Year in 1987?

5. Which French goalkeeper was bought by Manchester United in 2000 for £7.8 million?

6. How were Borotra, Lacoste, Cochet and Brugnon collectively known in the game of tennis?

7. Who won his first professional boxing bout in 1982, defeating Lupe Guerra at the Albert Hall?

8. Which Austrian skier won eight World Cup downhill races in 1975?

9. Which fielding position in cricket is closest to the wicket keeper?

10. Which Italian football star acquired the nickname of The White Feather?

ANSWERS

1. Face off 2. Featherweight 3. FIFA 4. Fatima Whitbread 5. Fabien Barthez
6. Four Musketeers 7. Frank Bruno 8. Franz Klammer 9. First slip 10. Fabrizio Ravanelli

QUIZ 22

. . . .

1 Which country hosts the first tennis Grand Slam tournament of the year?

2 Which Czech born player lost successive Wimbledon finals in 1986 and 1987?

3 In which decade were the Wimbledon championships first contested?

4 Which Swedish tennis star won the Australian Open, the French Open and the US Open in 1988?

5 How did Catherine McTavish make Wimbledon history in 1979?

6 Which Australian tennis star lifted the first two Men's Singles titles at Wimbledon in the 1970s?

7 Which commentator was known as, The Voice Of Wimbledon?

8 Who was the first woman to achieve the Grand Slam in tennis?

9 Which German tennis star was a surprise winner of the Men's Singles at Wimbledon in 1991?

10 Who was the only woman in the 20th century to win six consecutive Wimbledon titles?

ANSWERS

1. Australia 2. Ivan Lendl 3. 1870s 4. Mats Wilander 5. The first female umpire 6. John Newcombe 7. Dan Maskell 8. Maureen Connolly 9. Michael Stich 10. Martina Navratilova

QUIZ 23

•••••••••••••••••••••••••••••••

1 Prior to which annual event do the opposing captains toss an 1829 sovereign?

2 The Cincinnati Red Stockings were the first professional team in which sport?

3 In the game of association football, can a goal be scored direct from a throw in?

4 In which sport does John McCririck work as a TV presenter?

5 Which Manchester United star acquired the nickname of, The King in the 1960s?

6 The Concorde Agreement details the management guidelines in which sport?

7 Which was the third Asian country to play test cricket?

8 Which African nation were surprise scorers of the first goal in the 2002 soccer World Cup finals?

9 Which goalkeeper was presented with the FA Cup trophy in 1988 as Wimbledon captain?

10 Which three times Formula One world champion founded his own airline in Austria?

ANSWERS

1. Oxford & Cambridge boat race 2. Baseball 3. No 4. Horse racing 5. Denis Law 6. Formula One motor racing 7. Sri Lanka 8. Senegal 9. Dave Beasant 10. Niki Lauda

QUIZ 24

• •

All ten answers begin with the letter G

1. What is the alternative name for an up and under in rugby, named after the Irish club that invented it?

2. Who managed England at the 1998 World Cup finals?

3. In which sport has Larissa Latynina won eighteen Olympic medals?

4. Who trained Red Rum to three Grand National victories?

5. What is the nickname of Arsenal FC?

6. Who was crowned world's fastest woman, after winning the 100m gold medal at the 1992 Olympics?

7. Which annual race was first run at Wimbledon in 1985, having previously been staged at the White City?

8. Which king owned the racehorse that killed the suffragette Emily Davison?

9. Which state of the USA hosts the US Masters in the sport of golf?

10. Which legendary jockey was knighted by the newly crowned Queen Elizabeth II in 1953?

ANSWERS

1. Garryowen 2. Glenn Hoddle 3. Gymnastics 4. Ginger McCain 5. Gunners
6. Gail Devers 7. Greyhound Derby 8. George V 9. Georgia 10. Gordon Richards

QUIZ 25

- -

1   In the early days of boxing who acquired the nickname of, Homicide Hank?

2   What nickname is shared by Newcastle United FC and Notts County FC?

3   Which British sporting stadium is nicknamed The Cabbage Patch?

4   Which Australian snooker star was nicknamed Steady Eddie?

5   Which golfer is known as The Big Easy?

6   Who gave David Beckham the nickname of Goldenballs?

7   What connects the nicknames of Chicago's American football team and golfer Jack Nicklaus?

8   In which sport did Harry Wragg acquire the nickname of the Head Waiter?

9   Was the athlete Christopher Chataway nicknamed the Black Swan, the White Tiger or the Red Fox?

10 What nickname is shared by Wimbledon FC and Aberdeen FC?

ANSWERS

1. Hank Armstrong 2. Magpies 3. Twickenham 4. Eddie Charlton 5. Ernie Els 6. His wife, Victoria 7. Bears, Chicago Bears and the Golden Bear
8. Horse racing 9. Red Fox 10. The Dons

QUIZ 26

• •

1. What do the initials ITTF stand for?

2. Who won the Ryder Cup in 2002, Europe or the USA?

3. In American football, what is a Hail Mary?

4. Who won the greatest number of snooker world titles in the 1980s?

5. Which is the only weapon used in women's fencing?

6. Which country hosted the Commonwealth Games in 1930, 1954, 1978 and 1994?

7. How many people comprise a soling crew in Olympic yachting events?

8. Which former England test cricket captain penned an autobiography entitled, Opening Up?

9. In which decade was the Olympic games first televised?

10. For which county did Graham Gooch play county cricket?

ANSWERS

1. International Table Tennis Federation 2. Europe 3. A pass thrown a long distance 4. Steve Davis 5. Foil 6. Canada 7. Three 8. Michael Atherton 9. 1930s, the Berlin games of 1936 10. Essex

QUIZ 27

All ten answers begin with the letter H or I

1. Where is Happy Valley race course?

2. Which major trophy in the game of lacrosse was named after a tribe of native American Indians?

3. Maccabi Haifa are one of the leading soccer sides in which country?

4. What is the venue of the San Marino Grand Prix?

5. Which sports commentator penned the autobiography, Where's Harry?

6. In curling, what is the four-letter name for the starting line?

7. Which boxer did Dolph Lungren portray in the film Rocky IV?

8. In which ball sport is the Hummel Super Cup contested?

9. In 1989 which Norwegian female long distance runner triumphed in the Boston and New York marathons?

10. Which Swedish boxer was crowned world champion following a shock win over Floyd Patterson?

ANSWERS

1. Hong Kong 2. Iroquois Cup 3. Israel 4. Imola 5. Harry Carpenter 6. Hack
7. Ivan Drago 8. Handball 9. Ingrid Kristiansen 10. Ingemar Johannsen

QUIZ 28

1 In which event did US athlete Ed Moses win 122 consecutive races?

2 In athletics, what is a Western roll?

3 Which athlete retained his 1500m Olympic title at the 1984 games?

4 What is Carl short for in the name of Carl Lewis?

5 What nationality is the Olympic 1500m champion, Noureddine Morceli?

6 Which British athlete broke three world records in the space of nineteen days in 1985?

7 Which city hosted the 2002 European Athletics Championships?

8 How many hurdles does an athlete negotiate in a men's 110m hurdles race?

9 Which British city is home to an indoor athletics arena called the High Performance Centre?

10 Who broke the triple jump world record at the 1995 World Athletics Championships?

ANSWERS

1. 400m hurdles 2. A style of high jump 3. Sebastian Coe 4. Carlton
5. Algerian 6. Steve Cram 7. Munich 8. Ten 9. Birmingham 10. Jonathan Edwards

QUIZ 29

1. In which county is Market Rasen race course?

2. In 2001 who became the first Englishman for ten years to be crowned World Snooker Champion?

3. What sport is played by the Newcastle Falcons?

4. Which test venue is the home stadium of Warwickshire County Cricket Club?

5. In which city was the Knickerbocker Baseball Club founded?

6. What is the larger, a golf ball, a squash ball or a table tennis ball?

7. Was the boxer James Braddock nicknamed the Big Bad Wolf, the Cinderella Man or the Pied Piper?

8. In what decade were ball girls first used at Wimbledon?

9. In the past what has been won by Sergeant Murphy, Jack Horner, Oxo and Battleship?

10. What was named after Thomas Lord in 1787?

ANSWERS

1. Lincolnshire 2. Ronnie O'Sullivan 3. Rugby Union 4. Edgbaston 5. New York 6. Golf ball 7. The Cinderella Man 8. 1970s 9. The Grand National 10. Lord's cricket ground

QUIZ 30

All ten answers begin with the letter J or K

1 What is the nationality of the athlete Merlene Ottey?

2 Who was voted European Footballer of the Year in 1978 and 1979?

3 Which capital city hosted the 1998 Commonwealth Games?

4 Who won the women's tennis singles title at the 2002 Australian Open?

5 Which Scottish football club play their home matches at Rugby Park?

6 Which baseball team won the 1985 World Series?

7 Which football club won the 1996 European Champions Cup?

8 Who was the first cricketer to be named BBC Sports Personality of the Year?

9 Which Liverpool striker became the first player to miss a penalty at a Wembley FA Cup final?

10 Which football club replaced Chester in the football league in 2000?

ANSWERS

1. Jamaican 2. Kevin Keegan 3. Kuala Lumpur 4. Jennifer Capriati
5. Kilmarnock 6. Kansas City Royals 7. Juventus 8. Jim Laker 9. John Aldridge 10. Kidderminster

QUIZ 31

. . . .

1 Which city hosts the Indy 500 motor race?

2 Which cricket county play their home matches at the Racecourse Ground?

3 What prefix comes before the golf venues of Lytham, Birkdale and Troon?

4 Which city hosted the 2001 FA Cup final?

5 Which city is home to the snooker venue, The Crucible Theatre?

6 At which test cricket venue can spectators stand in the Radcliffe Road End?

7 Which Scottish football club were the first club to have an all seater stadium in Britain?

8 At Augusta golf course, all the holes are named after what?

9 Which Surrey town is home to the British National Shooting Centre?

10 At which racecourse do horses gallop across the Melling Road?

ANSWERS

1. Indianapolis 2. Derbyshire 3. Royal 4. Cardiff 5. Sheffield 6. Trent Bridge
7. Aberdeen 8. Plants and flowers 9. Bisley 10. Aintree

QUIZ 32

1 Which member of the royal family was voted BBC Sports Personality of the Year in 1971?

2 At the 2000 Olympics who won a boxing gold medal for Great Britain in the superheavyweight category?

3 Which motorcycle racing team did Giacomo Agostini become manager of on his retirement in 1975?

4 How many tennis courts are there at Wimbledon, eight, eighteen or twenty-eight?

5 In which athletics event did Jackie Joyner-Kersee break the world record?

6 Which sport was once known as, inanimate bird shooting?

7 In which African city was the 2003 cricket world cup final played?

8 In 2004, which Portuguese football star won his 100th international cap in a friendly against England?

9 In which South American country was the French rugby union star Serge Blanco born?

10 Who once said, "I am not having points taken off me by an incompetent fool. You are the pits of the world"?

ANSWERS

1. Princess Anne 2. Audley Harrison 3. Yamaha 4. Eighteen 5. Heptathlon
6. Clay pigeon shooting 7. Johannesberg 8. Luis Figo 9. Venezuela
10. John McEnroe

QUIZ 33

• •

All ten answers begin with the letter L

1   What do the letters LB stand for with regard to a position in American football?

2   What is the French word for a sled?

3   Who was the first cricketer to take 350 test wickets?

4   Which Italian club did Sven Goran Eriksson leave to become England manager?

5   What is Frankie short for in the name of the jockey Frankie Dettori?

6   Which sport was originally called bagataway?

7   Which British golfer won the 2004 Women's Australian Open?

8   Which boxing belt was named in 1909 after a Lord patron of the National Sporting Club?

9   Which British rugby league club are known as The Rhinos?

10 Who defeated Alaves 5-4 in the 2001 UEFA Cup final?

ANSWERS

1. Linebacker 2. Luge 3. Lance Gibbs 4. Lazio 5. Lanfranco 6. Lacrosse
7. Laura Davies 8. Lonsdale Belt 9. Leeds 10. Liverpool

QUIZ 34

• •

1. Which city hosted the World Cup in 1970 and 1986?

2. Penarol FC are a leading club in which South American country?

3. Who was the first player to score ten Premiership hat tricks in England?

4. Which goalkeeper scored one goal in 399 appearances for Manchester United?

5. Who do Nottingham Forest play in a local derby?

6. What nickname is shared by Boston United and Plymouth Argyle?

7. Which Merseyside team were originally called Domingo FC?

8. Which football club's fanzine is called The Flashing Blade?

9. By what score did Brazil beat Germany in the 2002 World Cup final?

10. Which football manager was sensationally sacked by Leeds United after just 44 days in charge in 1974?

ANSWERS

1. Mexico 2. Uruguay 3. Alan Shearer 4. Peter Schmeichel 5. Notts County
6. The Pilgrims 7. Everton 8. Sheffield United 9. 2-0 10 Brian Clough

QUIZ 35

. . . .

1   At the 1988 Seoul Olympics, what type of animal was the official mascot Hodori?

2   What flower is depicted on the badge of Glamorgan County Cricket Club?

3   What do the initials WR stand for with regard to a playing position in American football?

4   Who was the first President of the English Bowling Association?

5   What colour is the background of the Olympic flag?

6   What sport is played by the Scottish Eagles?

7   How many penalty points are conceded if a rider falls off a horse in show jumping competitions?

8   How many times was Bjorn Borg defeated in Wimbledon finals?

9   Which racecourse stages the Irish horseracing classics?

10 Which American football team did the legendary Pat Leahy play for in an eighteen year career?

ANSWERS

1. Tiger 2. Daffodil 3. Wide receiver 4. WG Grace 5. White 6. Ice hockey 7. 8 points 8. Once 9. The Curragh 10. New York Jets

QUIZ 36

All ten answers begin with the letter M

1 Which city is to host the 2006 Commonwealth Games?

2 What is the name of the home ground of Wolverhampton Wanderers FC?

3 Who was crowned world rally champion in 2002?

4 Which US state is home to the Hall of Fame of basketball?

5 Which sport on wheels made its Olympic debut in 1996?

6 Who lost his world middleweight title to Sugar Ray Leonard in 1987?

7 Who moved from Ayresome Park to the Riverside Stadium?

8 Which US baseball team are known as the Twins?

9 Who was crowned Formula One world champion in 1999?

10 Which New York venue is famed for staging world championship boxing bouts?

ANSWERS

1. Melbourne 2. Molineux 3. Marcus Gronholm 4. Massachusetts
5. Mountain biking 6. Marvin Hagler 7. Middlesbrough 8. Minnesota
9. Mika Hakkinen 10. Madison Square Garden

QUIZ 37

1 What was the final score of the 2003 rugby union World Cup final between England and Australia?

2 Which country joined the Five Nations Championships, to make it into the Six Nations Championships?

3 How many players from each side form a rugby union scrum?

4 In 2004 who replaced Martin Johnson as England rugby union captain?

5 Which nation were crowned rugby union world champios in 1995?

6 Which member of the British royal family is the patron of Scottish rugby union?

7 In 2004, which nation became the first team to beat the newly crowned world champions England?

8 Which rugby league team are nicknamed The Wires?

9 Which country did Jonah Lomu represent?

10 What is the name of the trophy presented to the winners of the rugby union world cup?

ANSWERS

1. England 20, Australia 17 2. Italy 3. Eight from each side 4. Lawrence Dallaglio 5. South Africa 6. Princess Anne 7. Ireland 8. Warrington 9. New Zealand 10. William Webb Ellis Trophy

QUIZ 38

1   What type of weapon features on the badge of Charlton Athletic FC?

2   How many Summer Olympic games were cancelled in the 20th century due to war?

3   What does a black flag signify in Formula One racing?

4   The Bill Shankly Stand is found at the home ground of which Lancashire football club?

5   Which world famous sporting team were originally called The Savoy Five?

6   Which tennis legend was the first man to achieve a Grand Slam?

7   Which was the first country to win cricket's world cup twice?

8   Which French striker moved from Fulham to Manchester United in 2004?

9   Which European nation did Brazil beat in the final when winning their first World Cup in 1958?

10 At the 1972 Munich Olympics, what breed of dog was the official mascot Waldi?

ANSWERS

1. A sword 2. Three 3. The disqualification of a driver 4. Preston North End
5. Harlem Globetrotters 6. Don Budge 7. West Indies 8. Louis Saha
9. Sweden 10. Dachshund

QUIZ 39

All ten answers begin with the letter N

1 Which was the first country to win 200 medals at the Winter Olympics?

2 Who was crowned World Superbike Champion in 2003?

3 On an ice hockey rink what is the area called between the defending blue line and the attacking blue line?

4 At which horseracing course were starting stalls first used?

5 Which country won football's African Nations Cup in 1994?

6 Which city hosted the 2002 Superbowl?

7 What does an umpire call for after every seven games at Wimbledon?

8 Which former Formula One world champion went on to compete in the Australian Open at golf?

9 In which country did the sport of korfball originate?

10 Which country hosted the first rugby union World Cup?

ANSWERS

1. Norway 2. Neil Hodgson 3. Neutral zone 4. Newmarket 5. Nigeria
6. New Orleans 7. New balls 8. Nigel Mansell 9. Netherlands 10. New Zealand

QUIZ 40

• •

1 Which Italian city is to host the 2006 Winter Olympics?

2 At which sport did Britain win its only gold medal at the 2002 Winter Olympics?

3 Which duo's autobiography is entitled, Facing The Music?

4 Which European nation hosted the first Winter Olympics?

5 What name is given to the member of a bobsleigh team who steers the sled?

6 What is an Hamill Camel?

7 Which EH won five gold medals at the 1980 Winter Olympics?

8 Which sport has categories called halfpipe, parallel slalom and giant slalom?

9 What mark is given to a perfect score in ice skating?

10 How many people comprise a curling team?

ANSWERS

1. Turin 2. Curling 3. Torvill and Dean 4. France 5. Pilot 6. A type of spin in ice skating 7. Eric Heiden 8. Snowboarding 9. Six 10. Four

QUIZ 41

• •

1 In which sport is Ty Cobb a famous name of the past?

2 Which watch manufacturer's name can be seen on the centre court scoreboard at Wimbledon?

3 Snatch and clean and jerk are both styles of what?

4 Which city hosted the Spanish Formula One Grand Prix in 2004?

5 Which British rugby league team are known as The Vikings?

6 Which Romanian tennis star lost Wimbledon finals to Stan Smith and Bjorn Borg?

7 In the world of sport, what measures 3.7m by 1.86m?

8 Which company sponsored the 2003 Grand National?

9 Which baseball team plays its home games at the Astrodome?

10 On what type of bars do women gymnasts compete?

ANSWERS

1. Baseball 2. Rolex 3. Weightlifting 4. Barcelona 5. Widnes 6. Ilie Nastase
7. A snooker table 8. Martell 9. Houston Astros 10. Asymmetric bars

QUIZ 42

• •

All ten answers begin with the letter O

1 What was the venue for the 2003 US Open in golf?

2 What was invented by the Scandanavian Ernst Killander?

3 Boundary Park is the home ground of which football club?

4 Which state of the USA is also the name for a defensive formation in American football?

5 Who kept goal for Bayern Munich in the 1999 European Cup final?

6 What is the nickname of Sheffield Wednesday FC?

7 Which horse won the Epsom Derby in 1999?

8 Which club won the Football League Cup in 1986?

9 Which is the only capital city to have hosted the Winter Olympics?

10 Which ground did Manchester United move to in 1910?

ANSWERS

1 Olympia Field 2. Orienteering 3. Oldham Athletic 4. Oklahoma 5. Oliver Kahn 6. Owls 7. Oath 8. Oxford United 9. Oslo 10. Old Trafford

QUIZ 43

1 Which legendary golfer won the British Open and the US Open in 1953?

2 In which golf Major is the winner presented with a green jacket?

3 How many shots under par is an eagle?

4 Who did Bernard Langer replace as Europe's Ryder Cup captain?

5 Which British golf course is home to the Valley of Sin?

6 Who won his first British Open in 2000?

7 In 2001, which British golfer sacked his caddy Miles Byrne?

8 What is the nationality of the golfer Vijay Singh?

9 What is the older, the US Open or the British Open?

10 In which US state is the US Masters traditionally held?

ANSWERS

1. Ben Hogan 2. US Masters 3. Two 4. Sam Torrance 5. St Andrews 6. Tiger Woods 7. Ian Woosnam 8. Fijiian 9. The British Open by 35 years 10. Georgia

QUIZ 44

• •

1 In which country did Muhammed Ali beat George Foreman in The Rumble In The Jungle?

2 On a golf course what is known as tiger country?

3 In which century was the Jockey Club founded?

4 What is the duration of a game of Gaelic football?

5 In which sport is Kareem Abdul-Jabbar a famous name?

6 In which city is the Hungarian Grand Prix held?

7 What nickname is shared by Oldham Athletic FC and Wigan Athletic FC?

8 Harry Gibbs, who retired in 1999 aged 79, was a famous what?

9 What sport is played by the Ottawa Senators?

10 Who did the Duke of York replace as the President of the Football Association?

ANSWERS

1. Zaire 2. Very deep rough 3. 18th century 4. 60 minutes 5. Basketball
6. Budapest 7. Latics 8. Boxing referee 9. Ice hockey 10. Duke of Kent

QUIZ 45

All ten answers begin with the letter P

1. Who was voted BBC Sports Personality of the Year in 2002?

2. What bird completes the name of Pittsburgh's ice hockey team?

3. What name is given to the playing area in the game of Gaelic football?

4. What is the nationalleague nickname of Yorkshire County Cricket Club?

5. Which horse did Carl Llewellyn ride to Grand National victory in 1992?

6. In the game of baseball which player stands on the mound in the middle of the playing area?

7. On a real tennis court, what name is given to the sloping roof of the gallery surrounded by three sides?

8. In which sport do the USA play Mexico for the Manuel Avila Camacho Cup?

9. Which former tennis star married former James Bond actor George Lazenby in 2002?

10. What is the platform called on which a fencing bout takes place?

ANSWERS

1. Paula Radcliffe 2. Penguins 3. Parallelogram 4. Phoenix 5. Party Politics
6. Pitcher 7. Penthouse 8. Polo 9. Pam Shriver 10. Piste

QUIZ 46

• •

In which sports are the following terms used?

1　Full Nelson

2　Bosie

3　Ippon

4　Notre Dame Shift

5　Ozeki

6　Southpaw

7　Brill bend

8　Appel

9　Chukka

10　Mashie-niblick

ANSWERS

1 Wrestling 2. Cricket 3. Judo 4. American football 5. Sumo wrestling
6. Boxing 7. High jump 8. Fencing 9. Polo 10. Golf

QUIZ 47

. . . .

1 Did Chris Evert-Lloyd win more French Opens or more Wimbledon titles?

2 Which cricket county's badge depicts three swords?

3 What two colours are the bottom two rings on the Olympic flag?

4 In which city did Carl Lewis win four Olympic gold medals?

5 How many players comprise an American football team?

6 Which country hosted the 2004 European Nations Championships at football?

7 What has a minimum length of 260cm for men and 220cm for women?

8 For which Formula One team did David Coulthard drive in the 2004 season?

9 What was won in 1996 by a Dane, in 1997 by a German, in 1998 by an Italian and in 1999 by an American?

10 At which course is the Oaks horserace held?

ANSWERS

1. French Opens, seven in total 2. Middlesex 3. Yellow and green 4. Los Angeles 5. Eleven 6. Portugal 7. Javelin 8. McClaren 9. Tour de France 10. Epsom

QUIZ 48

• •

All ten answers begin with the letter R

1 What name is given to the type of bow that is used in Olympic archery competitions?

2 First presented in 1965, in which sport is the Harry Sunderland Trophy awarded?

3 Which city is home to the Interlagos Grand Prix circuit?

4 Who was a shock winner of the Men's Singles at Wimbledon in 1996?

5 Who captained the Australian cricket team to World Cup glory in 2003?

6 What is the nickname of snooker star Ronnie O'Sullivan?

7 Which boxer did Paul Newman portray in the film Somebody Up There Likes Me?

8 Ibrox Park is the home of which football club?

9 Which horse, partly owned by Alex Ferguson, won the 2000 Guineas in 2002?

10 Which Brazilian star was voted European Footballer of the Year in 1999?

ANSWERS

1. Recurve 2. Rugby League 3. Rio de Janeiro 4. Richard Krajicek 5. Ricky Ponting 6. Rocket 7. Rocky Graziano 8. Rangers 9. Rock of Gibraltar 10. Rivaldo

QUIZ 49

. . . .

From which countries do the following football teams hail?

1 Celta Vigo

2 Standard Liege

3 Vasco da Gama

4 NAC Breda

5 AJ Auxerre

6 Udinese Calcio

7 Grampus 8

8 Schalke 04

9 Brondby IF

10 Newell's Old Boys

ANSWERS

1. Spain 2. Belgium 3. Brazil 4. Netherlands 5. France 6. Italy 7. Japan
8. Germany 9. Denmark 10. Argentina

QUIZ 50

1 Which sporting body has the initials WPBSA?

2 In which sport did Gabriela Sabatini win an Olympic medal for Argentina?

3 In which sport did Jane Couch acquire the nickname of the Fleetwood Assassin?

4 The Leander Club is the world's oldest club in which sport?

5 Who has defeated Chris Evert, Zena Garrison, Hana Mandlikova and Andrea Jaeger in Wimbledon finals?

6 Which world famous horse race celebrated its centenary in 1975?

7 In which decade did Wimbledon FC join the Football League?

8 In which sport are trousers called salopettes worn?

9 Who was the first woman to drive in a Formula One Grand Prix race?

10 In which sport did Rex Williams win his fourth world title in 1983?

ANSWERS

1 World Professional Billiards And Snooker Association 2. Tennis
3. Women's boxing 4. Rowing 5. Martina Navratilova 6. Kentucky Derby
7. 1970s 8. Skiing 9. Lella Lombardi 10 Billiards

QUIZ 51

All ten answers begin with the letter S

1. At which British racecourse is the Whitbread Gold Cup run?

2. Who did the USA oppose in 1994, in the first soccer World Cup match to be played indoors?

3. Which golfer was Europe's youngest representative in the 1999 Ryder Cup?

4. What S word is the name given to the pacesetter of a rowing team?

5. In which sport is the Jarvis Cup contested?

6. In which sport is the goal called a hail?

7. Which boxer who twice defeated Chris Eubank is nicknamed The Celtic Warrior?

8. Who scored 10,122 runs in 125 test matches for India?

9. What is the name of the female counterpart of the Ryder Cup?

10. Roger Federer was the first man from which country to win a tennis Grand Slam title?

ANSWERS

1. Sandown 2. Switzerland 3. Sergio Garcia 4. Stroke 5. Squash 6. Shinty 7. Steve Collins 8. Sunil Gavaskar 9. Solheim Cup 10. Switzerland

QUIZ 52

• •

1 Who became World Snooker Champion at his first attempt in 1972?

2 In which country did the game of snooker originate?

3 Who was the first World Snooker Champion?

4 Which Scottish snooker star is known as, The Wizard of Wishaw?

5 Who lost five consecutive world championship snooker finals in the 1990s?

6 Which Canadian acquired the nickname of, The Grinder?

7 How many red balls are on the table at the start of a frame?

8 In which decade was the World Snooker Championship first contested?

9 What would a players break be if potting three reds, one blue, one green and one black?

10 Who recovered from 8-0 down in the 1985 world final to take the title on the final black ball?

ANSWERS

1. Alex Higgins 2. India 3. Joe Davis 4. John Higgins 5. Jimmy White
6. Cliff Thorburn 7. Fifteen 8. 1920s 9. Eighteen 10. Dennis Taylor

QUIZ 53

. . . .

1. Which city's baseball team are known as The Padres?

2. Which country does the cricket star Saeed Anwar represent at test level?

3. Which horse did not run like a snail when winning the 1975 Grand National?

4. The Riverside Ground on Chester-le-Street is the home of which cricket county?

5. In 1995 which British driver was crowned World Rally Driving Champion?

6. Which footballer who starred in the film Escape To Victory, helped Brazil to win three World Cups?

7. In which sport is the Bob Hope Classic contested?

8. Other than tennis, in which sport has Ann Jones won the English Open?

9. Is the height of a tennis net 81cm, 91cm or 101cm?

10. What was Michael Angelow the first person to do at Lord's?

ANSWERS

1. San Diego 2. Pakistan 3. L'Escargot 4. Durham 5. Colin Macrae 6. Pelé
7. Golf 8. Table tennis 9. 91cm 10. Streak

QUIZ 54

All ten answers begin with the letter T

1 What plant is depicted on a Scottish rugby union shirt?

2 At which Scottish golf course did Greg Norman win the British Open in 1986?

3 What is the name of the corner that horses gallop around when approaching the straight at Epsom racecourse?

4 What type of wrestling involves two pairs of fighters?

5 Which element with the symbol of W is used in the manufacture of darts?

6 In which sport can a competitor perform a randolph and a rudolph?

7 Which country hosted football's African Nations Cup in 2004?

8 Who was the first golfer to record a televised hole in one?

9 What is the name of the Sydney stadium that hosted the 2003 rugby union World Cup final?

10 In which town is St James Street cricket ground, the home of Somerset CCC?

ANSWERS

1. Thistle 2. Turnberry 3. Tattenham Corner 4. Tag team wrestling
5. Tungsten 6. Trampolining 7. Tunisia 8. Tony Jacklin 9. Telstra 10. Taunton

QUIZ 55

. . . .

1 In what year was Nigel Mansell crowned Formula One World Champion?

2 Which car manufacturer made his Formula One debut in Australia in March 2002?

3 What was the nationality of the first six winners of the Tour de France?

4 Which manufacturer won the Formula One Constructors title in 2000, 2001, 2002 and 2003?

5 Which Brazilian driver was crowned Formula One Champion in 1981?

6 In Formula One racing, what colour of flag indicates that a driver should slow down and hold position?

7 Who broke the world land speed record in 1997 in a vehicle called Thrust SSC?

8 At which Grand Prix venue was Ayrton Senna killed?

9 In which city is the motor racing venue the Circuit de Catalunya?

10 Which Formula One hero was Scottish Junior Kart Champion from 1983 to 1985?

ANSWERS

1. 1992 2. Toyota 3. The French 4. Ferrari 5. Nelson Piquet 6. Yellow
7. Andy Green 8. San Marino 9. Barcelona 10. David Coulthard

QUIZ 56

. . . .

1 Which was the first German city to host the Summer Olympics?

2 In which county is Newton Abbot race course?

3 Which Texan town is home to the sporting stadium known as the Alamodome?

4 Is the North Sea Cup contested in swimming, windsurfing or rowing?

5 Which large animal features on the badge of Coventry City FC?

6 Which is the longer race, the Kentucky Derby or the Epsom Derby?

7 Which fencing weapon has a V shaped blade and a curved handle?

8 In which sport is the Golden Gloves Tournament contested?

9 Which football club's ground is situated on Stanley Matthews Way?

10 What type of animal was Syd, one of the official mascots at the 2000 Sydney Olympics?

ANSWERS

1. Berlin 2. Devon 3. San Antonio 4. Windsurfing 5. Elephant 6. Epsom Derby 7. Sabre 8. Amateur boxing 9. Stoke City 10. Platypus

QUIZ 57

All ten answers begin with the letter W

1　Which golfing trophy was instigated by the grandfather of George Bush?

2　Westmorland and Cumberland are both types of what?

3　Founded in 1920, what do the initials WBA stand for?

4　Spencer Gore, Frank Hadow and John Hartley were the first three men's winners at which sporting tournament?

5　From what wood are cricket bats traditionally made?

6　Which country hosted the Commonwealth Games in 1958?

7　Which team won the FA Cup in 1968?

8　Who recorded the song One Moment In Time, in celebration of the 1988 Olympics?

9　Which cricket county won the Benson & Hedges Cup in 2002?

10　Which football club is associated with the song, I'm Forever Blowing Bubbles?

ANSWERS

1. Walker Cup 2. Wrestling 3. World Boxing Association 4. Wimbledon
5. Willow 6. Wales 7. West Bromwich Albion 8. Whitney Houston
9. Warwickshire 10. West Ham United

QUIZ 58

1 In 1983 which Norwegian athlete became the first woman to lift the Marathon world title?

2 Which British track hosted the first ever Formula One world championship race in 1950?

3 In which country was the first ever cricket test match staged?

4 Who was the first French footballer to score in an FA Cup final?

5 Who was the first woman to train a Grand National winner?

6 Who were the first winners of the FA Cup?

7 Who was the first Scottish driver to be crowned Formula One World Champion?

8 Who was the first baseball player to score three home runs in a World Series?

9 In what year did Steffi Graf win her first Grand Slam title?

10 What was first held in 1978 and was contested from the capital of France to the capital of Senegal?

ANSWERS

1. Grete Waitz 2. Silverstone 3. Australia 4. Eric Cantona 5. Jenny Pitman
6. Wanderers 7. Jim Clark 8. Babe Ruth 9. 1987 10. Paris – Dakar Rally

QUIZ 59

1. What sport is played by the Phoenix Suns?

2. Which club's official address is Highbury Avenell Road, London?

3. Which 125-1 outsider became a Wimbledon champion in 2001?

4. Which US city is home to an American football team known as The Lions?

5. What do the initials HW signify with regard to a cricket dismissal?

6. In which sport might a competitor perform a J lean during a Liffey descent?

7. Andy Goram represented Scotland at football and which other sport?

8. Which colourful team won the Superbowl in 1997?

9. In which ball sport does the term "pegging out" mean finishing?

10. Which event comprises of swimming, cross country running, riding, fencing and pistol shooting?

ANSWERS

1. Basketball 2. Arsenal 3. Goran Ivanisevic 4. Detroit 5. Hit wicket
6. Canoeing 7. Cricket 8. Green Bay Packers 9. Croquet 10. Modern
pentathlon

QUIZ 60

. . . .

Unravel the anagrams to give the name of a football team

1 A RAM RIDDLE

2 COYEST KIT

3 BEEN A RED

4 CAFÉ BIN

5 LEARN AS

6 DENY TORY CUB

7 A BENCHED TWO

8 UNBAR CHIMNEY

9 EEL CASH

10 POLAR VET

ANSWERS

1. Real Madrid 2. Stoke City 3. Aberdeen 4. Benfica 5. Arsenal 6. Derby County 7. Cowdenbeath 8. Bayern Munich 9. Chelsea 10. Port Vale

QUIZ 61

• •

1   Which British football club won their third European Cup in 1981?

2   Which Irish manager left the English club Leicester City to manage the Scottish club Celtic?

3   Which club moved from London to Milton Keynes in 2003?

4   What did the Charity Shield change its name to?

5   Who did Tottenham Hotspur defeat in the first all London FA Cup final?

6   Which African nation inflicted a shock 3-0 defeat on Scotland in the 1998 World Cup finals?

7   Which football star of yesteryear, nicknamed the Gentle Giant, passed away in 2004?

8   Which football star is the son of the former rugby league star Danny Wilson?

9   Which country was the host nation for the 1978 World Cup?

10 Which Suffolk soccer side won the FA Cup in 1978?

ANSWERS

1. Liverpool 2. Martin O'Neill 3. Wimbledon 4. Community Shield
5. Chelsea 6. Morocco 7. John Charles 8. Ryan Giggs 9. Argentina
10. Ipswich Town

QUIZ 62

- -

1. In the sport of hurling how many points are scored if the ball passes under the bar?

2. Who did England meet in the first ever international soccer match?

3. What colour is the home strip of Real Madrid FC?

4. In which sport are the terms firer, kitty and tuck in used?

5. In what year did Boris Becker first lift the Wimbledon Singles title?

6. Which annual event was originally called the Liverpool Steeplechase?

7. In which decade was the world snooker championships staged at the Crucible for the first time?

8. Which forty year old goalkeeper won a World Cup winners medal in 1982?

9. Who was the only Australian to win the Men's Singles at Wimbledon in the 1980s?

10. Which jungle creature provides the nickname of Hull City FC?

ANSWERS

1. Three points 2. Scotland 3. White 4. Bowls 5. 1985 6. Grand National
7. 1970s 8. Dino Zoff 9. Pat Cash 10. The Tigers

QUIZ 63

. . . .

Unravel the anagrams to give the names of ten
   famous football stars

1   LOAN ROD

2   A LEAN RASHER

3   A RIGHT WIN

4   BOMBER BOYO

5   WHOLE CINEMA

6   COMPELS BALL

7   A CONCERTINA

8   ASH RUIN

9   A YELL ECHOS

10   NIFTY OMEN

ANSWERS

QUIZ 64

1 What do the initials MVP stand for in American sports?

2 How many umpires oversee a game of baseball?

3 Which tennis star won the US Open in 1997 and 1998?

4 With which American football team did Joe Montana win four Superbowls?

5 Which American football team are known as The Vikings?

6 In baseball which fielding position is situated behind the home plate?

7 Which team won its first Superbowl in 1998?

8 Why do American footballers paint black marks on their faces?

9 In North America, which unusual sport is also known as birling?

10 What links the American football teams from Baltimore, Atlanta and Seattle?

ANSWERS

1. Most valuable player 2. Four 3. Pat Rafter 4. San Francisco 49ers
5. Minnesota 6. Catcher 7. Denver Broncos 8. To protect against the sun's glare 9. Log rolling 10. Birds, Baltimore Ravens, Atlanta Falcons, Seattle Seahawks

QUIZ 65

1 In which decade did Fred Perry win three consecutive Wimbledon titles?

2 Which English football club were the first to score nine goals in a Premiership match?

3 What is the nationality of the motor racing driver Jarno Trulli?

4 Which sporting venue is located at St John's Wood, London?

5 Who lost football World Cup finals in 1966 and 1982?

6 Which post did Antonio Samaranch hold from 1980 to 2001?

7 What is the nickname of Australias national rugby league team?

8 What do the initials WA signify on a netball bib?

9 Who won Olympic gold performing to a piece of music entitled Bolero?

10 From which European country does the football team Rosenborg hail?

ANSWERS

1. 1930s 2. Manchester United 3. Italian 4. Lords 5. West Germany
6. President of the International Olympic Committee 7. Kangaroos 8. Wing attack 9. Torvill and Dean 10. Norway

QUIZ 66

• •

Unravel the anagrams to give the names of ten sports

1 ANT BELL

2 LION BATH

3 OWN RIG

4 ROMAN HAT

5 BALLET BASK

6 ENGINEER RIOT

7 RED SAGES

8 SWIRL GENT

9 PAROLE TWO

10 A BIRDS ILL

ANSWERS

QUIZ 67

1 What type of animal was Misha, the official mascot of the Moscow Olympics?

2 Which country provided the majority of the athletes for the first modern Olympics of 1896?

3 Which British athlete battled to the Olympic gold medal in the 1972 Women's Pentathlon?

4 Which sport regained Olympic status in 1988 after a 64 year absence?

5 Which country does the 2000 Olympic champion Haile Gebrselassie represent?

6 What is the highest city to have hosted the Summer Olympic games?

7 Which was the first city to host the modern Olympic games twice?

8 Which female athlete won five gold medals for the USA at the 2000 games?

9 Over how many days is an Olympic decathlon contested?

10 Who won four gold medals in 1936, much to the chagrin of Adolf Hitler?

ANSWERS

1. Bear 2. Greece 3. Mary Peters 4. Tennis 5. Ethiopia 6. Mexico City 7. Paris
8. Marion Jones 9. Two days 10. Jesse Owens

QUIZ 68

• •

1. What is the nationality of the soccer star Jaap Stam?

2. How old was Boris Becker when he won his first Wimbledon title?

3. Which nation won the first cricket World Cup for men?

4. Which nation won the first cricket World Cup for women?

5. Australia's national team for which sport are known as the Kookaburras?

6. Who won an FA Cup winners medal in 1988 and an Empire Award for Best British Actor in 2001?

7. Who did Jack Dempsey oppose in the boxing bout known as, The Fight Of The Long Count?

8. In which sport are a triangle and a spider used?

9. Who replaced Sharp as shirt sponsors for Manchester United?

10. Which London club did Arsenal defeat in the 2002 FA Cup final?

ANSWERS

1. Dutch 2. Seventeen 3. West Indies 4. England 5. Field hockey 6. Vinnie Jones 7. Gene Tunney 8. Snooker 9. Vodafone 10. Chelsea

QUIZ 69

• •

Unravel the anagrams to give the name of a piece of
    sporting equipment

1　CRAB TICKET

2　SECURE NOOK

3　BALLET INNS

4　BASKET ROAD

5　DANISH RUG

6　A MERLIN POT

7　CLAN FORGER

8　SHELVING A TOUR

9　TOTS CHUCKLE

10　PLY COINAGE

ANSWERS

1. Cricket bat 2. Snooker cue 3. Tennis ball 4. Skateboard 5. Shinguard
6. Trampoline 7. Corner flag 8. Vaulting horse 9. Shuttlecock 10. Clay
pigeon

QUIZ 70

1. Which horse overtook Crisp in the final stretch to win the 1973 Grand National?

2. In which century was the Epsom Derby first contested?

3. Which course stages the Lincoln Handicap, the first major race of the British flat season?

4. Which Irish jockey, who rode his first winner on Alvaro in 1969, announced his retirement in 2003?

5. Which Grand National winning horse of 1991 shared it's name with the sponsors of the race?

6. Who is the only jockey to win nine Epsom Derbys?

7. Which comedian owned the 1994 Grand National winner Minnehoma?

8. Who was the first woman to ride in the Epsom Derby?

9. In which month of the year is the Cheltenham Festival traditionally held?

10. Which champion jockey rode nearly 9000 winners in a forty year career from 1949 to 1989?

ANSWERS

1. Red Rum 2. 18th century 3. Doncaster 4. Pat Eddery 5. Seagram
6. Lester Piggott 7. Freddie Starr 8. Alex Greaves 9. March 10. Willie Shoemaker

QUIZ 71

. . . .

1 Who won his first Wimbledon title in 1974 and his last in 1982?

2 Which country's Formula One Grand Prix is held at Zandvoort?

3 Who sang at the opening ceremonies of the 1994 soccer World Cup and 1995 rugby union World Cup?

4 What are cyclist doing when they are honking?

5 In which sport is the term wishbone ketch used?

6 Which British capital is home to the Millennium Stadium?

7 Which cricket county plays its home matches at Old Trafford?

8 Who was the first Irish cyclist to win the Tour de France?

9 Who managed Celtic FC to European Cup glory in 1967?

10 Which British airport has in the past staged the Grand National?

ANSWERS

1. Jimmy Connors 2. Netherlands 3. Diana Ross 4. Standing out of the saddle 5. Yachting 6. Cardiff 7. Lancashire 8. Stephen Roche 9. Jock Stein 10. Gatwick

QUIZ 72

• •

Unravel the anagrams to give the names of ten male
   tennis stars

1   PREFER DRY

2   EMMA NINTH

3   ROCKIER EBBS

4   AFTER TRAP

5   A RED SIN SAGA

6   BASER FED GENT

7   PAMPERS A SET

8   ROVER LAD

9   LEND ANVIL

10   MINT STASH

ANSWERS

1. Fred Perry 2. Tim Henman 3. Boris Becker 4. Pat Rafter 5. Andre Agassi
6. Stefan Edberg 7. Pete Sampras 8. Rod Laver 9. Ivan Lendl 10. Stan Smith

QUIZ 73

• •

1 What score in darts is known as "bed & breakfast"?

2 Which Welshman was the first darts world champion?

3 On a dartboard what number is sandwiched by 19 and 17?

4 What is the four-letter name given to the platform from which a player throws the darts?

5 How many points is the outer ring of the bullseye worth?

6 Who was the first darts player to score a televised 501 nine dart finish?

7 Which 80s world champion was nicknamed, The Milky Bar Kid?

8 Which Lancashire born comedian presented the TV gameshow Bullseye?

9 What is the highest score that can be achieved with one dart?

10 What is the home city of Eric Bristow?

ANSWERS

1. 26 2. Leighton Rees 3. Three 4. Oche 5. 25 6. John Lowe 7. Keith Deller
8. Jim Bowen 9. 60 10. London

QUIZ 74

• •

1 In which sport was the Gordon Bennett Trophy instigated?

2 Which nation did Alf Ramsey describe as, "animals" in the 1966 World Cup?

3 Which sport was devised by the Australians Tom Willis and Henry Harrison?

4 In the 2004 Formula One season which racing team did Jarno Trulli drive for?

5 What type of animal was Amik, the official mascot for the 1976 Montreal Olympics?

6 The Rose Bowl, The Orange Bowl, The Cotton Bowl and The Sugar Bowl are all contested in which sport?

7 Which city hosts the US Open in tennis?

8 At which sport do the Firebrands face Indian Gymkhana?

9 What does the acronym BAR stand for with regard to the Formula One motor racing team?

10 Which decade witnessed the first Winter Paralympics?

ANSWERS

1. Motor racing 2. Argentina 3. Australian rules football 4. Renault
5. Beaver 6. American football 7. New York 8. Field hockey 9. British
American Racing 10. 1970s, 1976 in Sweden

QUIZ 75

• •

Identify the world snooker champions from their
    initials and the year they won the title

1   2002   PE

2   1997   KD

3   1982   AH

4   1977   JS

5   1986   JJ

6   1974   RR

7   1991   JP

8   1966   JP

9   1979   TG

10 1951   FD

ANSWERS

QUIZ 76

- -

1 In the 1966 World Cup final between England and West Germany what was the score after 90 minutes?

2 From which Scottish club did Alex Ferguson join Manchester United?

3 What is the significance of English football clubs who sport triangular flags on their corner flags?

4 John Toshack and Mark Hughes have both managed which national team?

5 Who scored 48 goals for England and a century for the MCC at Lord's?

6 In which London football stadium can the fans watch the game from the comfort of the Matthew Harding Stand?

7 Which African nation won the football gold medal at the 2000 Sydney Olympics?

8 Which british football club lost in the final of the 2003 UEFA Cup?

9 What is the name of the park that separates Goodison Park and Anfield?

10 In which country is the headquarters of UEFA?

ANSWERS

1. 2-2 2. Aberdeen 3. This means they have won the FA Cup 4. Wales
5. Gary Lineker 6. Stamford Bridge, home of Chelsea 7. Cameroon 8. Celtic
9. Stanley Park 10. Switzerland

QUIZ 77

. . . .

1   In which athletic event did Daley Thompson break the world record on four occasions?

2   At which university were the first set of codified rules for American football formulated?

3   Which sport features in the Britney Spears video for the song, Baby One More Time?

4   Which cricket sporting body instigated the first set of rules for lawn tennis?

5   In which water based event did Birgit Fischer become the first woman to win Olympic gold at four games?

6   In which sport is the Solheim Cup contested?

7   Which Grand Slam event takes place at the Roland Garros Stadium?

8   Which Scottish golf course hosted the 2002 British Open?

9   Which annual race has been sponsored by ADT, Flora, Mars and Guinness?

10 Who completes the 2000 gold medal quartet of Steve Redgrave, Tim Foster and James Cracknell?

ANSWERS

1. Decathlon 2. Harvard 3. Basketball 4. MCC 5. Canoeing 6. Golf, women's golf 7. French Open in tennis 8. Muirfield 9. London Marathon 10. Matthew Pinsent

QUIZ 78

• •

In which countries are the following Winter Olympic
venues?

1 Innsbruck

2 Squaw Valley

3 Nagano

4 St Moritz

5 Grenoble

6 Calgary

7 Lillehammer

8 Cortina d'Ampezzo

9 Sarajevo

10 Sapporo

ANSWERS

1. Austria 2. USA 3. Japan 4. Switzerland 5. France 6. Canada 7. Norway
8. Italy 9. Yugoslavia 10. Japan

QUIZ 79

1 Which cricket legend scored the first ever Test Match century?

2 How many runs are scored if the ball hits a fielder's helmet on the ground?

3 What is the home ground of Yorkshire CCC?

4 Who captained Australia from 1984 to 1994?

5 In which stadium does the Ashes Trophy permanently reside?

6 What five-letter D word is the name given to an easy catch in cricket?

7 Which county joined the County Championships in 1992?

8 What animal features on the badge of Leicestershire CCC?

9 Who was the last England cricket captain of the 20th century to win an Ashes series?

10 Which Australian cricket star was banned from using an aluminium bat called The Combat?

ANSWERS

1. WG Grace 2. Five 3. Headingley 4. Allan Border 5. Lord's 6. Dolly
7. Durham 8. Fox 9. Mike Gatting 10. Dennis Lillee

QUIZ 80

1 In which sport is a contest known as, The Hawaiian Ironman contested?

2 In the 20th century who managed the national soccer teams of England and Australia?

3 Who officially opened the Commonwealth Games in 2002?

4 In which sport is the Giro D'Italia a major competition?

5 Which team does the Italian football club Juventus play in a local derby?

6 Which Scottish born jockey won the Epsom Derby on Troy and Henbit?

7 What is the nationality of the Formula One star Rubens Barrichello?

8 How many periods comprise an ice hockey game?

9 In which sport is the Jim Thorpe Trophy presented to the most valuable player?

10 At which race track can drivers travel at great speed down the Jack Brabham Strait?

ANSWERS

1. Triathlon 2. Terry Venables 3. Queen Elizabeth II 4. Cycling 5. Torino
6. Willie Carson 7. Brazilian 8. Three 9. American football 10. Brands Hatch

QUIZ 81

. . . .

The following ten answers all contain the words Tom,
Dick or Harry

1 Which British sports star was nicknamed, The
Preston Plumber?

2 Who wrote the horseracing thrillers Smokescreen
and Field Of Thirteen?

3 Who managed Portsmouth FC to Premiership
promotion in 2003?

4 Which golfer won the British Open and the US
Open in 1982?

5 Who won the gold medal for the men's high
jump in the 1968 Summer Olympics?

6 In a 1997 novel who caught the golden snitch to
win a game of quidditch?

7 Which boxer nicknamed, The Duke held the WBO
heavyweight title and starred in the film Rocky V?

8 Which New Jersey born ice skater was a five times
world champion before becoming a TV
commentator?

9 Which footballer was voted Young PFA Player of
the Year in 2000?

10 In 1924 who won a 100m Olympic gold medal, a
feat chronicled in the film Chariots Of Fire?

ANSWERS

1. Tom Finney 2. Dick Francis 3 Harry Redknapp 4. Tom Watson 5. Dick
Fosbury 6. Harry Potter 7. Tommy Morrison 8. Dick Button 9. Harry Kewell
10. Harold Abrahams

QUIZ 82

1. At which Brazilian club did Pele spend the majority of his career?

2. In September 1996, which jockey rode all seven winners at an Ascot meeting?

3. Which knighted cricket star has the middle names of St Auburn?

4. Who overcame cancer to win the 1999 Tour de France?

5. How many golf majors did Jack Nicklaus win in his pro career. Was it eight, eighteen or twenty-eight?

6. Who was awarded a controversial draw in a 1999 boxing bout against Evander Holyfield?

7. Which team did the basketball superstar Michael Jordan lead to six NBA titles?

8. Which rugby union star scored 64 tries in 101 appearances for Australia between 1982 and 1996?

9. Under what name does Terry Bollea step into the wrestling arena?

10. Which tennis star retired in 1999 shortly after winning her 22nd Grand Slam title?

ANSWERS

1. Santos 2. Frankie Dettori 3. Sir Garfield Sobers 4. Lance Armstrong
5. Eighteen 6. Lennox Lewis 7. Chicago Bulls 8. David Campese 9. Hulk Hogan 10. Steffi Graf

QUIZ 83

• •

1 What was the surname of the cricket after whom the bosie or the googly was named?

2 What name is given to the craft of making arrows?

3 Which city hosts Argentina's Formula One Grand Prix?

4 What is the name of the home ground of Leicestershire CCC?

5 In which country was the sports star Jahangir Khan born?

6 Which nation won the first soccer World Cup for women?

7 Which American golfer won the British Open in 1998?

8 Which Asian country was granted Test cricket status in 2000?

9 Which astronaut represented the USA, carrying the Olympic flag at the Sydney Olympics?

10 Who captained Brazil's 1970 World Cup winning team?

ANSWERS

1. Bosanquet 2. Fletching 3. Buenos Aires 4. Grace Road 5. Pakistan 6. USA
7. Mark O'Meara 8. Bangladesh 9. John Glenn 10. Carlos Alberto

QUIZ 84

- -

1 What S is Australian cricket's equivalent of extras?

2 What P is the name given to the round stump on a horse's saddle?

3 What R is the name for the red and white peg in the game of croquet?

4 In fencing what P is 14m long and 1.5m wide?

5 What N is a ski slope for novice skiers?

6 What F is the playing area of a golf hole between the green and the tee?

7 What does the U stand for in the acronym UEFA?

8 What B is a combination of rifle shooting and cross country skiing?

9 What A is the name for the last runner in a relay race?

10 What C defeated Argentina in the opening match of soccer's World Cup in 1990?

ANSWERS

1. Sundries 2. Pommel 3. Rover 4. Piste 5. Nursery 6. Fairway 7. Union , Union of European Football Association 8. Biathlon 9. Anchor 10. Cameroon

QUIZ 85

• •

1   Which boxer was known as The Punching Preacher in his comeback fights?

2   Who did Sugar Ray Leonard oppose in The Brawl In Montreal?

3   What is the duration of a boxing round?

4   Which boxer lived up to his nickname of The Real Deal when he was crowned World Champion in 1990?

5   What beastly name is given to an illegal punch to the back of a boxer's head?

6   Who did Muhammed Ali nickname, The Ugly Bear?

7   What do the initials BBBC stand for?

8   Who lost five fights against Sugar Ray Robinson and was later portrayed in the film Raging Bull?

9   Who did Muhammed Ali defeat in The Thriller In Manila?

10 Which boxer hung up his gloves in 1955 with a perfect record of 49 wins in 49 fights?

ANSWERS

1. George Foreman 2. Roberto Duran 3. Three minutes 4. Evander Holyfield
5. Rabbit punch 6. Sonny Liston 7. British Boxing Board of Control 8. Jake
LaMotta 9. Joe Frazier 10. Rocky Marciano

QUIZ 86

• •

1 What name is shared by the 2000 winner of the Grand National and a 1973 film starring Steve McQueen?

2 What took place in Manchester in 2002 from July 25 to August 4?

3 Which town stages the Monaco Grand Prix?

4 Which crafty cockney won his first world title in 1980?

5 What name is given to the target area in a game of curling?

6 With which county did Geoff Boycott spend the majority of his cricket career?

7 Which position in rugby union wears the number nine shirt?

8 What sport is played by the Helsinki Roosters?

9 Which British horseracing course is also known as Prestbury Park?

10 What is the nationality of the football star Henrik Larsson?

ANSWERS

1. Papillon 2. The Commonwealth Games 3. Monte Carlo 4. Eric Bristow
5. House 6. Yorkshire 7. Scrum-half 8. American football 9. Cheltenham
10. Swedish

QUIZ 87

Do the following American based sports teams play ice hockey, American football, baseball or basketball?

1 Florida Marlins

2 San Jose Sharks

3 Carolina Panthers

4 Cleveland Cavaliers

5 Minnesota Timberwolves

6 Philadelphia Eagles

7 Phoenix Coyotes

8 Baltimore Orioles

9 Dallas Stars

10 Atlanta Hawks

ANSWERS

1. Baseball 2. Ice hockey 3. American football 4. Basketball 5. Basketball
6. American football 7. Ice hockey 8. Baseball 9. Ice hockey 10 Basketball

QUIZ 88

• •

Which football club plays their home matches at …

1 The Riverside Stadium?

2 Hillsborough?

3 Vicarage Road?

4 Ewood Park?

5 The Bescot Stadium?

6 Portman Road?

7 Fratton Park?

8 Pride Park?

9 Ashton Gate?

10 Gresty Road?

ANSWERS

1. Middlesbrough 2. Sheffield Wednesday 3. Watford 4. Blackburn Rovers
5. Walsall 6. Ipswich Town 7. Portsmouth 8. Derby County 9. Bristol City
10. Crewe Alexandra

QUIZ 89

• •

1. What was Margaret Court's last name when she won her first Wimbledon title?

2. Which Australian landmark was depicted on the Sydney Olympic torch?

3. In which country was the National Hockey League founded in 1917?

4. Diomed was the first ever winner of which race?

5. What stands 3m from the floor and has a diameter of 45.74cm?

6. In which cathedral city is the home ground of Kent CCC?

7. What is the alternative name for an ace in the game of golf?

8. How many innings comprise a game of baseball?

9. Mills Lane is a leading referee in which sport?

10. Who captained the West Indies cricket team from 1974 to 1985?

ANSWERS

1. Smith 2. Sydney Harbour Bridge 3. Canada 4. Epsom Derby 5. Basketball hoop 6. Canterbury 7. Hole in one 8. Nine 9. Boxing 10. Clive Lloyd

QUIZ 90

• •

Unravel the anagrams to give the names of ten female
    tennis stars

1　MAIN HAIR STING

2　SURE BREAK

3　SLICE SO MEAN

4　LUVS A WIN SMILE

5　MY RIPER ACE

6　RICHER VETS

7　VERA SHRIMP

8　A SCATTY RUIN

9　RAIDING A VIEW

10　A MARSEILLES WIN

ANSWERS

1. Martina Hingis 2. Sue Barker 3. Monica Seles 4. Venus Williams 5. Mary
Pierce 6. Chris Evert 7. Pam Shriver 8. Tracy Austin 9. Virginia Wade
10. Serena Williams

QUIZ 91

1 Who was the shock winner of the Men's Singles at Wimbledon in 1996?

2 On what surface is the French Open played?

3 Who was the first British female tennis player to win eight Grand Slam events?

4 At the 2001 Wimbledon championships who was the only British seeded player in the Men's Singles?

5 After which tennis star was the showcourt at Flushing Meadows in New York renamed?

6 What is the official name of Wimbledon?

7 Which country knocked Australia out of the 2004 Davis Cup?

8 Who won the US Open in 2001 and Wimbledon in 2002 in the Men's Singles?

9 How old was Michael Chang when he won the French Open in 1989?

10 How many times did Bjorn Borg face John McEnroe in Wimbledon finals?

ANSWERS

1. Richard Krajicek 2. Clay 3. Ann Jones 4. Tim Henman 5. Arthur Ashe
6. All England Lawn Tennis and Croquet Club 7. Sweden 8. Lleyton Hewitt
9. Seventeen 10. Two

QUIZ 92

. . . .

1 Which Australian city hosted the 1962 Commonwealth Games?

2 Which FIFA president gave his name to the first World Cup trophy?

3 The Diamondbacks are a baseball team from which US state?

4 What colour are the home shirts of Nigeria's international soccer team?

5 Which Scottish village annually hosts the Highland Games in early September?

6 Who, at the age of 71, managed a football team in England's Premiership in 2004?

7 Which female tennis star won an Olympic gold medal for the USA in 1996?

8 Which cricket nation were granted Test Match status in 1928?

9 Dr Frank Stableford devised a scoring system for which sport?

10 Which was the first football team to achieve the FA Cup and League Championship double?

ANSWERS

1. Perth 2. Jules Rimet 3. Arizona 4. Green 5. Braemar 6. Sir Bobby Robson
7. Lindsay Davenport 8. West Indies 9. Golf 10. Preston North End

QUIZ 93

• •

In which event did the following athletes win Olympic gold for Britain?

1. Ann Packer
2. Chris Finnegan
3. Adrian Moorhouse
4. Jason Queally
5. Tessa Sanderson
6. Eric Liddell
7. Allan Wells
8. Mary Rand
9. Mary Peters
10. Sally Gunnell

ANSWERS

1. 800m 2. Boxing 3. 100m breaststroke 4. Cycling 5. Javelin 6. 400m
7. 100m 8. Long jump 9. Pentathlon 10. 400m hurdles

QUIZ 94

• •

In which sport are the following trophies contested?

1 Wightman Cup

2 America's Cup

3 Westchester Cup

4 Uber Cup

5 Cheltenham Gold Cup

6 Calcutta Cup

7 Copa America

8 Curtis Cup

9 Currie Cup

10 Iroquois Cup

ANSWERS

1. Tennis 2. Yachting 3. Polo 4. Badminton 5. Horse racing 6. Rugby union
7. Soccer 8. Golf 9. Cricket 10. Lacrosse

QUIZ 95

1 Which British city hosted the Commonwealth Games in 1970 and 1986?

2 In 1903, the Boston Red Sox were the first winners of which sporting event?

3 At which sport did Precious McKenzie represent Great Britain?

4 In which country is the Suzuka Grand Prix circuit?

5 Which cricket county plays its home fixtures at the St Lawrence ground?

6 In 1998 which teenager became the youngest male swimming world champion in the history of the sport?

7 Which WWE wrestler is nicknamed Stone Cold?

8 What nickname is shared by Manchester United FC and Belgium's national soccer team?

9 In which sport are Robert Sangster and Vincent O'Brien both famous names?

10 On which piece of winter sports equipment is the seat called a sling?

ANSWERS

1. Edinburgh 2. World Series in baseball 3. Weightlifting 4. Japan 5. Kent
6. Ian Thorpe 7. Steve Austin 8. Red Devils 9. Horse racing 10. Luge

QUIZ 96

• •

How many players comprise a …

1 Rugby union team?

2 Australian rules football team?

3 Baseball team?

4 Volleyball team?

5 Rugby league team?

6 Netball team?

7 Polo team?

8 Field hockey team?

9 Basketball team?

10 Men's lacrosse team?

ANSWERS

1. 15 2. 18 3. 9 4. 6 5. 13 6. 7 7. 4 8. 11 9. 5 10. 10

QUIZ 97

• •

Identify the cities that hosted the Summer Olympics
from their initial letters and given years

1   1992   B
2   1964   T
3   1972   M
4   1928   A
5   1952   H
6   1960   R
7   1996   A
8   1976   M
9   1956   M
10 1920   A

ANSWERS

1. Barcelona 2. Tokyo 3. Munich 4. Amsterdam 5. Helsinki 6. Rome
7. Atlanta 8. Montreal 9. Melbourne 10. Antwerp

QUIZ 98

1 SW 19 is the postcode of which sporting venue?

2 What type of bird was Sam, the official mascot of the 1984 LA Olympics?

3 In which sport did the phrase, to win hands down originate?

4 Abner Doubleday is known as, the Father of what?

5 What is the nationality of the soccer star Henning Berg?

6 Bunny Austin was the first player to wear what on the Wimbeldon centre court?

7 Who did Wisden's Almanac name as India's Cricketer of the Century?

8 In which country was the jockey Willie Carson born?

9 Who won a gold medal at the 1972 Olympics and married a British princess a year later?

10 Who managed Nottingham Forest to European Cup glory in consecutive years?

ANSWERS

1. Wimbledon 2. Eagle 3. Horse racing 4. Baseball 5. Norwegian 6. Shorts
7. Kapil Dev 8. Scotland 9. Captain Mark Phillips 10. Brian Clough

QUIZ 99

• •

Which sports feature in the following films?

1 Slapshot

2 The Waterboy

3 The Hurricane

4 Fever Pitch

5 Downhill Racer

6 Space Jam

7 California Dolls

8 Major League

9 Tin Cup

10 Blackball

ANSWERS

1. Ice hockey 2. American football 3. Boxing 4. Soccer 5. Skiing
6. Basketball 7. Women's wrestling 8. Baseball 9. Golf 10. Crown green
bowling

QUIZ 100

· ·

1 In which sport can competitors take a practice shot known as a bluffie?

2 In which sport do the Brighton Bears play the Chester Jets?

3 Soling and Finn are both categories in which sport?

4 What sport uses a basket called a cesta?

5 In which sport are two or four players overseen by thirteen officials?

6 The Grand Hussars were the first team in England to play which sport?

7 What game uses four red balls, four white balls and one black ball?

8 In which athletic event was a technique called the O'Brien Shift named after Parry O'Brien?

9 At which sport do the Glamorgan Dragons play the Surrey Lions?

10 Which sport uses the term, bedposts in the alley?

ANSWERS

1. Archery 2. Basketball 3. Yachting 4. Pelota 5. Tennis 6. Polo 7. Bagatelle
8. Shot putt 9. Cricket 10. Ten pin bowling

QUIZ 101

. . . .

1 Which teenage tennis star acquired the nickname of The Swiss Miss?

2 What sport is played by the Scottish Claympres?

3 For which nation did Donovan Bailey win Olympic gold?

4 Carrow Road is the home ground of which football club?

5 What is the national martial art of Korea?

6 Which sport is James M Naismith credited with inventing in 1891?

7 In which city is the Edgbaston cricket stadium?

8 Who was the first boxer to receive a knighthood?

9 What was won in the 1980s by Golden Fleece, Secreto and Slip Anchor?

10 In which city do the Valiants play the Potters in a local soccer derby?

ANSWERS

1. Martina Hingis 2. American football 3. Canada 4. Norwich City 5. Tae kwan do 6. Basketball 7. Brimingham 8. Henry Cooper 9. Epsom Derby 10. Stoke

QUIZ 102

1 Which SH was World Snooker Champion in 1999?

2 Which LC was BBC Sports Personality of the Year in 1993?

3 Which SE won the US Open at tennis in 1990?

4 Which PS won the US Open at golf in 1999?

5 Which NF won the British Open at golf in 1992?

6 Which CR won the baseball World Series in 1990?

7 Which ES won the Grand National in 1998?

8 Which CC won the FA Cup in 1987?

9 Which SLR won the Superbowl in 2000?

10 Which RR won the Scottish League Cup at soccer in 1995?

ANSWERS

1. Stephen Hendry 2. Linford Christie 3. Stefan Edberg 4. Payne Stewart
5. Nick Faldo 6. Cincinnati Reds 7. Earth Summit 8. Coventry City 9. St
Louis Rams 10. Raith Rovers

QUIZ 103

1 What country does the athlete Frankie Fredericks represent?

2 Which fellow Brit was the great rival of Sebastian Coe in the 1980 Olympics?

3 Over what distance are Olympic rowing races for men contested?

4 Who was the first man to successfully defend a 100m Olympic title on the track?

5 At which event did Lynn Davies win Olympic gold for Great Britain?

6 In which city was the Moroccan athlete Said Aouita born?

7 Which British track athlete recounted her career in the book, Running Tall?

8 In which country was Zola Budd born?

9 In 1988 who became the first woman to throw the javelin beyonf 80m?

10 Which British athlete, born in Gateshead, set three world records in 1985 in the space of twenty days?

ANSWERS

1. Namibia 2. Steve Ovett 3. 2000m 4. Carl Lewis 5. Long jump 6. Rabat
7. Sally Gunnell 8. South Africa 9. Petra Felke 10. Steve Cram

QUIZ 104

. . . .

1   In which sport might a player stand at silly mid off?

2   Which sport derived from a game called sphairistrike?

3   Which England international footballer played for Marseilles in the 1991 European Cup final?

4   What animal features on the badge of Millwall FC?

5   What was named after the winter sportsman Ulrich Salchow?

6   Who was the first Formula One driver to be named BBC Sports Personality of the Year?

7   In which sport did Steve Cauthen acquire the nickname of the Kentucky Kid?

8   Videoton FC hail from which European country?

9   What is the maximum number of sets that can be played in a women's tennis match?

10 In which sport is the Waterloo Cup contested in the seaside town of Blackpool?

ANSWERS

1. Cricket 2. Tennis 3 Chris Waddle 4. Lion 5. A figure skating jump
6. John Surtees 7. Horse racing 8. Hungary 9. Three 10. Crown green
bowling

QUIZ 105

• •

What are the nationalities of the following Formula
One World Champions?

1   1972   Emerson Fittipaldi

2   1977   Niki Lauda

3   1980   Alan Jones

4   1993   Alain Prost

5   1967   Denny Hulme

6   2000   Michael Schumacher

7   1999   Mika Hakkinen

8   1979   Jody Scheckter

9   1952   Alberto Ascari

10   1982   Keke Rosberg

ANSWERS

1. Brazilian 2. Austrian 3. Australian 4. French 5. New Zealander 6. German
7. Finnish 8. South African 9. Italian 10. Finnish

QUIZ 106

. . . .

1 In which sport has Graham Henry coached Wales?

2 Does a squash ball weigh 24gms, 34gms or 44gms?

3 Which sport features the playing positions of first defence, second attack and in home?

4 What sport derived from the ancient game of paganica?

5 Which sport uses balls coloured red, yellow, blue and black and six hoops?

6 Shakoor Rana and David Shepherd are both officials in which sport?

7 Three cushions is a variety of which ball sport?

8 In which team sport is the Cowdray Park Gold Cup contested?

9 In volleyball, what is the maximum number of times a team can touch a ball before it crosses the net?

10 FLAT LOBS is an anagram of which sport?

ANSWERS

1. Rugby union 2. 24gms 3. Lacrosse 4. Golf 5. Croquet 6. Cricket, both umpires 7. Billiards 8. Polo 9. Three times 10. Softball

QUIZ 107

1 In Ireland, what do the initials GAA signify in the world of sport?

2 In what month of the year is the Epsom Derby traditionally held?

3 Who did Muhammed Ali defeat to win his first world title?

4 Which nation's national soccer team are nicknamed The Socceroos?

5 In which country was Ivan Lendl born?

6 How many oars does a rower use in a sculling race?

7 In Association football what has a minimum height of 1.52m?

8 Which was the first Asian country to host the Summer Olympics?

9 Who was the first Formula One driver to win five world championships?

10 In which sport would Sean Cerly take a penalty corner?

ANSWERS

1. Gaelic Athletic Association 2. June 3. Sonny Liston 4. Australia
5. Czechoslovakia 6. Two 7. Corner flags 8. Japan 9. Juan Manuel Fangio
10. Field hockey

QUIZ 108

. . . .

Identify the BBC Sports Personality of the Year from
their initials and their sport

1   2001   DB   Football

2   1993   LC   Athletics

3   1985   BM   Boxing

4   1988   SD   Snooker

5   1981   IB   Cricket

6   1997   GR   Tennis

7   1983   SC   Athletics

8   1990   PG   Football

9   1987   FW   Athletics

10 1960   DB   Showjumping

ANSWERS

1. David Beckham 2. Linford Christie 3. Barry McGuigan 4. Steve Davis
5. Ian Botham 6. Greg Rusedski 7. Steve Cram 8. Paul Gascoine 9. Fatima
Whitbread 10. David Broome

QUIZ 109

• •

1 Which Argentine midfield star scored for Spurs in the 1981 FA Cup final?

2 From which club did Chelsea sign Damien Duff?

3 In which city do Hearts play their home games?

4 What is the nationality of the football star Luis Figo?

5 Who was manager of Manchester United when they won the FA Cup in 1983 and 1985?

6 What animals are depicted on England's national shirt?

7 Who managed Germany to World Cup glory in 1990 after previously captaining the team to win the World Cup?

8 In 2002, who at 22 became the youngest player to captain England?

9 By what name are football linesmen now known?

10 Who managed England at Euro 96?

ANSWERS

1. Ricky Villa 2. Blackburn Rovers 3. Edinburgh 4. Portuguese 5. Ron Atkinson 6. Lions 7. Franz Beckenbauer 8. Michael Owen 9. Assistant referees 10. Terry Venables

QUIZ 110

. . . .

1 The Oval is the home ground of which cricket county?

2 What is the weight of the men's discus?

3 Was the sport of volleyball founded in Maine, Massachusetts or Maryland?

4 What is the home country of the tennis star David Nalbandian?

5 For which team did Damon Hill win the 1996 Formula One world title?

6 In which sport is an electronic eye known as The Cyclops used?

7 What does the letter C indicate on a netball bib?

8 In what year did Maradona score his "hand of God " goal against England?

9 Founded in 1880, which organisation has the initials AAA?

10 In which sport are Jack Hobbs and Wally Hammond both famous names of the past?

ANSWERS

1. Surrey 2. 2kg 3. Massachusetts 4. Argentina 5. Williams 6. Tennis
7. Centre 8. 1986 9. Amateur Athletics Association 10. Cricket

QUIZ 111

Identify the American football teams from their initials letters

1 The W   Redskins

2 The C   Bengals

3 The LA Raiders

4 The TB Buccaneers

5 The T   Titans

6 The M   Vikings

7 The B   Ravens

8 The NE Patriots

9 The D   Broncos

10 The C   Bears

ANSWERS

1. Washington 2. Cincinnati 3. Los Angeles 4. Tampa Bay 5. Tennessee
6. Minnesota 7. Baltimore 8. New England 9. Denver 10. Chicago

QUIZ 112

. . . .

1 In which city was the final of the 2003 rugby union World Cup played?

2 Which playing position in rugby union is situated in the middle of the front row?

3 Which rugby league team plays its home matches at the Don Valley Stadium?

4 Against which country did Italy record its first Six Nations championships victory in 2004?

5 Which Yorkshire club won the Rugby League Challenge Cup in 2003?

6 Which nation won the Six Nations Championships in 2003?

7 Which rugby league team won the rugby union Middlesex Sevens Tournament in 1996?

8 Which two countries contest the Calcutta Cup in rugby union?

9 What colour are the home shirts of France's national team?

10 What colour are the shirts traditionally worn by the Barbarians?

ANSWERS

QUIZ 113

· ·

1   In which decade was the first Olympic marathon for women contested?

2   What is the predominant colour on the cover of Wisden's Cricket Almanac?

3   Which island is home to Queen's Park Oval test cricket ground?

4   At the start of a frame of snooker, what colour of ball lies nearest to the green ball?

5   From which country do the football club Dynamo Minsk hail?

6   Did the long jump world record held by Bob Beamon last for 13 years, 23 years or 33 years?

7   Which ground hosted the first ever cricket test match played in England?

8   Did Willie Carson win the Epsom Derby three times, four times or five times?

9   How many Winter Olympic Games were cancelled in the 20th century due to war?

10 After which politician is the home stadium of Washington Redskins named?

ANSWERS

1. 1980s, the 1984 Olympics 2. Yellow 3. Trinidad 4. Brown ball 5. Belarus
6. 23 years 7. Kennington Oval 8. Four times 9. Two 10. Robert F Kennedy

QUIZ 114

• •

re the following statements fact or fib?

1 In the game of cricket there are 12 different ways to be dismissed

2 Lester Piggott was just 12 years of age when he rode his first winner

3 The first team sport contested in the modern Olympics was water polo

4 Sylvester Stallone was inspired to make the film Rocky after watching Henry Cooper fight Muhammed Ali

5 Rolf Harris is a former junior javelin champion in Australia

6 General George Patton represented the USA in the Olympic Games in the pentathlon event

7 In 2000, Mark Williams became the first left-handed player to be crowned Snooker World Champion

8 In the 20th century. Mike Tyson was the youngest boxer to win a world title

9 The sport of kendo was named after Ken Do Wong

10 Only thirteen countries competed in the first soccer World Cup in 1930

ANSWERS

1. Fib, there are only 10 2. Fact 3. Fact 4. Fib, the boxer in question was Chuck Wepner 5. Fib, a former swimming champion 6. Fact 7. Fact 8. Fib, Wilfred Benitez won a world title at 17 9. Fib 10. Fact

QUIZ 115

- -

1 Who managed Sunderland to FA Cup glory in 1973?

2 Who was crowned Formula One World Champion in 1998?

3 Which nation wrested the America's Cup from the USA in 1983?

4 In which sport is Kornelia Ender a past Olympic champion?

5 Who won three successive Wimbledon titles from 1991 to 1993?

6 Which horse won the 2003 Epsom Derby?

7 Who beat Liverpool 2-0 at Anfield in May 1989 to clinch the league title?

8 Twin sisters Diane and Rosalind Rowe have won over 20 national titles in which sport?

9 Who retired at the age of 26 having won five consecutive Wimbledon titles?

10 Who captained West Ham to FA Cup glory, when he was just 23 years old in 1964?

ANSWERS

1. Bob Stokoe 2. Mika Hakkinen 3. Australia 4. Swimming 5. Steffi Graf
6. Kris Kin 7. Arsenal 8. Table tennis 9. Bjorn Borg 10. Bobby Moore

QUIZ 116

1 Which sports company's logo is known as, the Swoosh?

2 In which sport is the All Ireland final contested at Croke Park?

3 In which race do competitors pass under Hammersmith Bridge and Barnes Bridge?

4 Which race is known as, The Run For The Roses?

5 How many points are awarded for a converted kick following a rugby union try?

6 In which city was the golfer Gary Player born?

7 Which Irish jockey rode the winning horses in the Prix de l'Arc de Triomphe in 1985. 1986 and 1987?

8 Which German international striker of yesteryear was nicknamed, Der Bomber?

9 The modern rules of which game were established by a Scottish solicitor called William M Mitchell?

10 Which American football team plays its home matches at the Mile High Stadium?

ANSWERS

1. Nike 2. Gaelic football 3. Oxford and Cambridge boat race 4. Kentucky Derby 5. 2 points 6. Johannesburg 7. Pat Eddery 8. Gerd Muller 9. Crown green bowls 10. Denver Broncos

QUIZ 117

•••••••••••••••••••••••••••••

Who are the following quotes and statements
attributed to?

1 There are some people on the pitch. They think its
   all over, it is now.

2 The car is unique, except for the one behind
   which is identical.

3 Float like a butterfly, sting like a bee.

4 I'm sick to death of my World Cup winning drop
   goal.

5 You cannot be serious!

6 Golf is a good walk spoiled.

7 Of course I'm pleased to get lucky 2000 times, but
   now I'd like to ride another 2000 winners.

8 It's a funny thing, the more I practice the luckier I
   get.

9 I needed two stitches after Alex kicked that boot
   at me.

10 Some people think football is a matter of life and
   death. I assure you, its much more serious than
   that.

ANSWERS

1. Kenneth Wolstenholme, commentator at the 66 World Cup 2. Murray
Walker 3. Muhammed Ali 4. Jonny Wilkinson 5. John McEnroe 6. Mark
Twain 7. Jockey Tony McCoy 8. Arnold Palmer 9. David Beckham 10. Bill
Shankly

QUIZ 118

. . . .

1 Which team won the 1983 FA Cup final and were relegated in the same year?

2 In what year did Bjorn Borg lose his first Wimbeldon final?

3 Who lost in the final of the World Snooker Championships in 1998 and 2003?

4 Who lost to Serena Williams in the Wimbledon finals of 2002 and 2003?

5 Which nation were the losing finalists in crickets World Cup in 1975 and 1996?

6 Which football club lost three FA Cup finals in the 1980s?

7 Which team were the losers in the 2003 Superbowl?

8 Which boxer lost his world title in 1990 in a shock defeat to Buster Douglas?

9 Which nation were the losing finalists in soccer's World Cup in 1974 and 1975 despite playing "total football"?

10 Which player lost consecutive Men's Singles finals at Wimbledon in 2000 and 2001?

ANSWERS

1. Brighton 2. 1981 3. Ken Doherty 4. Her sister Venus Williams 5. Australia
6. Everton 7. Oakland Raiders 8. Mike Tyson 9. Netherlands or Holland
10. Pat Rafter

QUIZ 119

1 In 1930 which country hosted the inaugural Commonwealth Games?

2 In which sport is the Alfred Dunhill Cup contested?

3 Which was the first Asian country to host a Formula One Grand Prix race?

4 At which sport do the Utah Jazz play at The Salt Palace?

5 In which decade did Liverpool FC win their first European Cup?

6 Which sporting team are nicknamed The Bronx Bombers?

7 In March 2004, which team knocked Manchester United out of the European Cup?

8 Neil Adams represented Great Britain in which sport?

9 What connects the Formula One world champions of 1968 and 1996?

10 What nationality are the soccer stars Mark Viduka and Harry Kewell?

ANSWERS

1. Canada 2. Golf 3. Japan 4. Basketball 5. 1970s 6. New York Yankees
7. Porto 8. Judo 9. Father and son, Graham and Damon Hill 10. Australian

QUIZ 120

1 Which is the longer race, the Grand National or the Oxford & Cambridge Boat Race?

2 Which is the heavier fencing weapon, an epee or a foil?

3 Is Martina Navratilova right handed or left handed?

4 Did Stirling Moss ever win the Formula One world title

5 Which country staged golf's first British Open, England or Scotland?

6 Which is the heavier boxing category, flyweight or strawweight?

7 In pro baseball games do the home team or the away team always bat first?

8 Is Brighton racecourse in East Sussex or West Sussex?

9 Which university won the 2003 Boat Race, Oxford or Cambridge?

10 Who is the older football brother, Phil Neville or Gary Neville?

ANSWERS

1. Grand National 2. Epee 3. Right handed 4. No 5. Scotland 6. Flyweight
7. Away team 8. East Sussex 9. Oxford 10. Gary Neville

QUIZ 121

. . . .

1 In the game of golf, what is a golden ferret?

2 Who did Tiger Woods replace as the No 1 ranked golfer in 1998?

3 What name is given to a golf course situated near the coast?

4 Which US golfer is nicknamed, Boom Boom?

5 Other than England or Scotland, which is the only country to hosted the British Open?

6 Which golfer won the British Open in 2001?

7 Which popular golfer's motto is, "grip it and rip it"?

8 What five-letter word prefixes the golf course of Troon, Lytham and Birkdale?

9 Was the first US Open played in New Jersey, Maine or Rhode Island?

10 Who won the US Masters in 1986 at the age of 46?

ANSWERS

1. Holing out from a bunker 2. Greg Norman 3. Links 4. Fred Couples
5. Ireland 6. David Duvall 7. John Daly 8. Royal 9. Rhode Island 10. Jack Nicklaus

QUIZ 122

1 Which country is to host the 2008 Summer Olympics?

2 In which sport has Prince Charles played on the same team as his sons William and Harry?

3 Which country's Formula One Grand Prix is staged at Estoril?

4 In which sport was Jonah Barrington the British Open Champion on six occasions?

5 How many throwing events are there in a heptathlon?

6 The 1981 Wimbledon mixed doubles title was won by which brother and sister?

7 Which city is home to the Bislett Athletics Stadium?

8 What sport do Cambridge University play at a venue called Fenner's?

9 What are the two official colours of the All England Lawn Tennis And Croquet Club?

10 What perfect score in ten pin bowling is achieved by rolling twelve consecutive strikes?

ANSWERS

1. China 2. Polo 3. Portugal 4. Squash 5. Two 6. Tracy and John Austin
7. Oslo 8. Cricket 9. Purple and green 10. 300

QUIZ 123

• •

1   I was born in Scotland and I captained the victorious Ryder Cup team in 2002. Who am I?

2   I was born in Dallas in 1967 and at the 1996 Olympics I set a new world record for the 200m. Who am I?

3   I am a famous pugilist who was born in 1923 and I died in a plane crash in 1969. Who am I?

4   I was born in Christchurch in 1951 and I took 431 Test wickets for New Zealand. Who am I?

5   I was born in County Antrim in 1974 and in 2002 I rode 269 winners in a single season. Who am I?

6   I was born in 1943 and in 1971 I became the first sportswoman to earn $100,000 in a year. Who am I?

7   I was born in 1965 and from 1988 to 1996 I captained England's rugby union team. Who am I?

8   I was born in Northumberland in 1937 and scored 49 goals in 106 matches for England. Who am I?

9   I was born in Devon in 1901 and in 1967 I sailed around the world in Gypsy Moth IV. Who am I?

10   I was born in California in 1950 and collected 7 gold medals in 1972. Who am I?

ANSWERS

1. Sam Torrance 2. Michael Johnson 3. Rocky Marciano 4. Richard Hadlee
5. Tony McCoy 6. Billie Jean King 7. Will Carling 8. Bobby Charlton 9. Sir
Francis Chichester 10. Mark Spitz

QUIZ 124

. . . .

1   Which snooker star was world champion on seven occasions in the 1990s?

2   What nationality is the snooker star Terry Griffiths?

3   What colour of ball follows the brown in order of points value?

4   Which snooker star acquired the nickname of The Golden Nugget?

5   What colour are the gloves worn by a snooker referee?

6   In the game of snooker what is a kick?

7   How many points are conceded if commiting a foul stroke on the pink ball?

8   Who founded The Matchroom Organisation?

9   Which snooker star of the 70s and 80s was nicknamed The Silver Fox?

10 Was the snooker star Marco Fu born in England, Thailand or Hong Kong?

ANSWERS

1. Stephen Hendry 2. Welsh 3. Blue 4. Steve Davis 5. White 6. A bad contact between the cue ball and the object ball 7. Six points 8. Barry Hearn 9. David Taylor 10. Hong Kong

QUIZ 125

. . . .

1   In which decade was the butterfly swimming stroke established in competition?

2   Which Canadian snooker star recorded the first televised 147 in the World Championships?

3   In which sport are the Southern Cross Series races contested?

4   What wild cat provides the nickname of Argentina's rugby union team?

5   What name is given to the front starting position on the grid of a Formula One race?

6   In May 1954 who famously wore the number 41 shirt in Oxford?

7   The Giants and The Jets are both American football teams from which city?

8   Which is the only British football league team that contains a day of the week in its name?

9   In which sport is the Harry Sunderland Trophy awarded?

10 Which US basketball team are known as The Lakers?

ANSWERS

1. 1950s 2. Cliff Thorburn 3. Yachting 4. Puma 5. Pole position 6. Roger Bannister 7. New York 8. Sheffield Wednesday 9. Rugby league 10. Los Angeles Lakers

QUIZ 126

. . . .

1 I was born in Kent in 1934 and I lost my title to Joe Bugner in 1971. Who am I?

2 I was born in Michigan in 1959 and in 1991 I was diagnosed HIV positive. Who am I?

3 I was born in Cardiff in 1940 and I became a world champion in 1970 sitting on Beethoven. Who am I?

4 I was born in France in 1943 and I won three downhill skiing Olympic gold medals in 1968. Who am I?

5 I was born in Georgia in 1886 and I was the first person to be elected to Baseball's Hall of Fame. Who am I?

6 I was born in 1945 and won 119 caps for Northern Ireland as a goalkeeper. Who am I?

7 I was born in 1967 and became the first unseeded player to win the Wimbledon Men's Singles. Who am I?

8 I was born in Spain in 1957 and in 1979 I became the youngest player to win the British Open. Who am I?

9 I was born in Italy in 1942 and won 15 world titles on two wheels between 1966 and 1975. Who am I?

10 I was born in Surrey in 1921 and my boat Bluebird was salvaged from Coniston Water in 2001. Who am I?

ANSWERS

1. Henry Cooper 2. Magic Johnson 3. David Broome 4. Jean Claude Killy
5. Ty Cobb 6. Pat Jennings 7. Boris Becker 8. Severiano Ballesteros
9. Giacomo Agostini 10. Donald Campbell

QUIZ 127

- -

1 Who managed Liverpool to a league and cup double in 1986?

2 Near which European capital city do Anderlecht play their home games?

3 Which club were promoted to the Football League in 2003 for the first time in their 103 year history?

4 By what three-letter name is the Brazilian star Eduardo Cesar Gaspar better known?

5 Which Newcastle starlet was voted Young PFA Player of the Year in 2003?

6 Which sea does Grimsby Town's football ground overlook?

7 Who wore the number 10 shirt for England in the 1966 World Cup final?

8 Who did Steve Staunton replace as captain of the Republic of Ireland team in the 2002 World Cup?

9 Which Hungarian soccer star of yesteryear was nicknaemd The Galloping Major?

10 Which Suffolk soccer side won the FA Cup in 1978?

ANSWERS

1. Kenny Dalglish 2. Brussels 3. Yeovil Town 4. Edu 5. Jermaine Jenas 6. North Sea 7. Geoff Hurst 8. Roy Keane 9. Ferenc Puskas 10. Ipswich Town

QUIZ 128

. . . .

1 What is the alternative name for an ace in the game of golf?

2 By what name was the legendary football star William Ralph Dean better known?

3 In which South African city is the Newlands cricket ground?

4 What six-letter word means, missing the ball in baseball and knocking down all the pins in ten pin bowling?

5 Which Nobel Peace Prize winner carried the Olympic flag for South Africa at the 2000 Sydney games?

6 Which country stages Grand Prix races at Spa-Francorchamps?

7 What number of shirt does Thierry Henry wear for Arsenal?

8 In which sport is Len Ganley a famous referee?

9 Dundee Shuffle and Yankee are both types of what?

10 Which team was coached by former All Blacks star John Kirwan at the 2004 Six Nations championships?

ANSWERS

1. Hole in one 2. Dixie Dean 3. Cape Town 4. Strike 5. Nelson Mandela
6. Belgium 7. 14 8. Snooker 9. Horse racing bets 10. Italy

QUIZ 129

1 I am the only Irishman in the 20th century to be voted European Footballer of the Year. Who am I?

2 I was born in London in 1931 and I was a co-founder of the London Marathon. Who am I?

3 I was born in Ontario in 1961 and became known as, The Great One in the game of ice hockey. Who am I?

4 I was born in Illinois in 1952 and won 125 singles titles in my tennis career. Who am I?

5 I was born in Belarus in 1956 and won three gymnastic gold medals at the 1972 Olympics. Who am I?

6 I was born in Lanarkshire in 1922 and I managed Scotland in the 1982 World Cup finals. Who am I?

7 I was born in London in 1950 and won world titles for Suzuki in 1976 and 1977. Who am I?

8 I was the first cricketer to play in 100 test matches for England and I was nicknamed Kipper. Who am I?

9 I was born in Ipswich in 1930 and in 1996 I created a company called F1 Management. Who am I?

10 I was born in Georgia in 1949 and I won my first heavyweight world title in 1978. Who am I?

ANSWERS

1. George Best 2. Christopher Chataway 3. Wayne Gretzky 4. Jimmy Connors 5. Olga Korbut 6. Jock Stein 7. Barry Sheene 8. Colin Cowdrey 9. Bernie Ecclestone 10. Larry Holmes

QUIZ 130

• •

Identify the sports stars from their initials and the titles
    of their autobiographies

1   VW   Courting Triumph

2   JP   Glorious Uncertainty

3   DG   Dazzler

4   FB   Eye Of The Tiger

5   JN   The Greatest Game Of All

6   DB   My Side

7   TB   Both Sides Of The Border

8   NL   To Hell And Back

9   VR   Sir Vivian, The Definitive Autobiography

10 JF   Born Lucky

ANSWERS

1. Virginia Wade 2. Jenny Pitman 3. Darren Gough 4. Frank Bruno 5. Jack
Nicklaus 6. David Beckham 7. Terry Butcher 8. Niki Lauder 9. Viv Richards
10. John Francome

QUIZ 131

. . . .

1 How many players comprise a hurling team?

2 What is the purpose of a sag wagon in cycling?

3 In which North American city are the Maple Leafs ice hockey team based?

4 In which sport is the Scobie Breasley Medal awarded?

5 Named after Debbie Brill, what is the Brill Bend?

6 On which island was the snooker star Tony Drago born?

7 In which sport did Rudy Hartono win the All England Championships on eight occasions?

8 Who recorded a long jump of 8.9m in the 1968 Mexico Olympics?

9 At which Scottish golf course is hole number 17 known as, The Road Hole?

10 By what shorter name is Florence Griffith-Joyner otherwise known?

ANSWERS

1. Fifteen 2. To pick up injured or withdrawn cyclists 3. Toronto 4. Horse racing 5. A style of high jump 6. Malta 7. Badminton 8. Bob Beamon 9. St Andrews 10. Flo-Jo

QUIZ 132

• •

1. I was born in Derbyshire in 1901 and I was the first player to make an official 147 break in snooker. Who am I?

2. I was born in France in 1955 and I was appointed FIFA Sports Director in 1998. Who am I?

3. I was born in London in 1918 and played cricket for Middlesex and England and football for Arsenal. Who am I?

4. I was born in 1956 and coached England to World Cup glory in 2003. Who am I?

5. I was born in Belfast in 1949 and my style of play earned me the nickname of The Hurricane. Who am I?

6. I was born in Bristol in 1957 and in 1997 I co-founded Adventure On Ice. Who am I?

7. I was born in Dundee in 1964 and in 1991 I was voted BBC Sports Personality of the Year. Who am I?

8. I was born in Cardiff in 1969 and won my first wheelchair London Marathon in 1992. Who am I?

9. I was born in California in 1961 and I became the first US cyclist to win the Tour de France. Who am I?

10. I was born in Melbourne in 1969, in 2003 I received a one year ban from the Australian Cricket Board. Who am I?

ANSWERS

1. Joe Davis 2. Michel Platini 3. Dennis Compton 4. Clive Woodward
5. Alex Higgins 6. Robin Cousins 7. Liz McColgan 8. Tanni Grey-Thompson
9. Greg Lemond 10. Shane Warne

QUIZ 133

1 In 2003, which car manufacturer won its first Le Mans 24 hour race since 1930?

2 Which team did Jensen Button drive for in the 2004 Formula One season?

3 Which ex World Champion on two wheels died in Australia in March 2003 aged 52?

4 What does the acronym NASCAR stand for?

5 Which Formula One world champion won the Indy Car Championship in 1993?

6 In which English county is Brooklands motor racing circuit?

7 Which country hosted the first Grand Prix race of the 2004 Formula One season?

8 How many championship points are awarded to the first placed driver in a Formula One Grand Prix race?

9 Which French motor racing champion was nicknamed The Professor?

10 In what year did Michael Schumacher win his first race in Formula One?

ANSWERS

1. Bentley 2. BAR 3. Barry Sheene 4. National Association Of Stock Car Auto Racing 5. Nigel Mansell 6. Surrey 7. Australia 8. Ten points 9. Alain Prost 10. 1993

QUIZ 134

• •

1 In which sport is the Dairylea Dunkers Championships contested?

2 Which city hosted the first Superbowl, was it Los Angeles, Chicago or New York?

3 In which sport has Claire Connor captained England?

4 What colour of ball was used in the 1973 FA Cup final?

5 In which county is Goodwood Park race course?

6 What does a green flag signify in motor racing?

7 What is the first event in a three day eventing competition?

8 In which sport is the movement of a projectile speeded up by sooping the ice?

9 Which was the first country to win soccer's World Cup twice?

10 To which sport did Lord Stanley donate the Stanley Cup?

ANSWERS

1. Basketball 2. Los Angeles 3. Cricket 4. Orange 5. West Sussex 6. Course is clear 7. Dressage 8. Curling 9. Italy 10. Ice hockey

QUIZ 135

. . . .

1 I was born in Quebec in 1950 and Montreal's Grand Prix circuit is named after me. Who am I?

2 I was born in Washington DC in 1971 and in 1993 I was the number one tennis player. Who am I?

3 I was born in 1971 and in 2001 I became the world's most expensive footballer. Who am I?

4 I was born in Pennsylvania in 1956 and helped the San Francisco 49ers win four Superbowls. Who am I?

5 I was born in Alabama in 1914 and I was champion of the world from 1937 to 1949. Who am I?

6 I was born in 1945 and in 1990 at the age of 45 I became the oldest player to win the US Open. Who am I?

7 I was born in Munich in 1945 and I coached Germany to World Cup glory in 1990. Who am I?

8 I was born in 1916, knighted in 1954, and the first pro captain of the England cricket team. Who am I?

9 I was born in Brazil in 1976 and won the French Tennis Open in 2000 and 2001. Who am I?

10 I was born in Yorkshire in 1963 and won 75 caps for England whilst playing club football for Arsenal. Who am I?

ANSWERS

1. Gilles Villeneuve 2. Pete Sampras 3. Zinedine Zidane 4. Joe Montana
5. Joe Louis 6. Hale Irwin 7. Franz Beckenbauer 8. Sir Len Hutton 9.
Gustavo Kuerten 10. David Seaman

QUIZ 136

• •

1 In 1909 who became the first black boxer to win the heavyweight world title?

2 What was the venue of the Ancient Olympics?

3 Whose statue complete with rugby ball can be found at Rugby School?

4 What two official colours were adopted by the MCC in Victorian times?

5 Who famously finished a game of bowls before facing the Spanish Armada?

6 Which race originated in 1903 as a result of a feud between two French sports newspapers?

7 Which organisation was founded at Newmarket in 1750?

8 Which South American country played host to soccer's first World Cup in 1930?

9 In 1871, the National Association became the first professional league in which US sport?

10 Which sports company has provided the tennis balls for the Wimbledon championships since 1902?

ANSWERS

QUIZ 137

1 Which test venue is the home ground of Middlesex CCC?

2 Which US city boasts a pro basketball, a pro ice hockey, a pro American football and two pro baseball teams?

3 How many players prior to Peter Shilton won 100 caps for England, 2, 3 or 4?

4 In which sport was Tony Allcock the indoor world champion in 2002?

5 On an archery target what colour is next to the gold bullseye?

6 Who was the first tennis star to be voted BBC Sports Personality of the Year?

7 Who captained the England cricket team from 1988 to 1993?

8 Which baseball team were involved in the Black Sox Scandal?

9 In 1972 who was crowned Formula One world champion at the age of 25?

10 Which English football club are nicknamed The Toffees?

ANSWERS

1. Lord's 2. Chicago 3. Three 4. Bowls 5. Red 6. Ann Jones 7. Graham Gooch 8. Chicago White Sox 9. Emerson Fittipaldi 10. Everton

QUIZ 138

• •

What is the home state of the following American
   football teams?

1 San Diego Chargers

2 Chicago Bears

3 Dallas Cowboys

4 Pittsburgh Steelers

5 Denver Broncos

6 Green Bay Packers

7 Detroit Lions

8 Indianapolis Colts

9 Miami Dolphins

10 Cleveland Browns

ANSWERS

1. California 2. Illinois 3. Texas 4. Pennsylvania 5. Colorado 6. Wisconsin
7. Michigan 8. Indiana 9. Florida 10. Ohio

QUIZ 139

• •

Identify the Scottish football clubs from their initials
and their nicknames

1 SM   The Buddies

2 AU   The Diamonds

3 BR   The Borderers

4 QP   The Spiders

5 ICT   The Jags

6 DU   The Terrors

7 FA   The Loons

8 HA   The Accies

9 DA   The Pars

10 AA   The Wasps

ANSWERS

1. St Mirren 2. Airdrie United 3. Berwick Rangers 4. Queens Park
5. Inverness Caledonian Thistle 6. Dundee United 7. Forfar Athletic
8. Hamilton Academicals 9. Dunfermline Athletic 10. Alloa Athletic

QUIZ 140

. . . .

1 What is the minimum age requirement for a horse in Olympic equestrian events?

2 What do the initials ITF stand for with regard to a sporting body?

3 Which sport is overseen by an official known as a gyogi?

4 Who acquired the nickname of The Long Fellow due to his unusual height for a jockey?

5 Which decade witnessed the first Paralympics?

6 In 1998, which nation won the first Olympic ice hockey title for women?

7 Which race was instigated by Carl Fisher in 1911?

8 Which football club changed it's nickname from The Rokerites to The Black Cats?

9 What do the initials RB stand for with regard to a playing position in American football?

10 In which country was the first golf club in North America founded?

ANSWERS

1. Seven 2. International Tennis Federation 3. Sumo wrestling 4. Lester Piggott 5. 1960s, first games held in Rome in 1960 6. USA 7. Indianapolis 500 8. Sunderland 9. Running back 10. Canada

QUIZ 141

In which counties are the following football clubs based?

1 Luton Town

2 Preston North End

3 Reading

4 Gillingham

5 Plymouth Argylle

6 Yeovil Town

7 Southampton

8 Boston United

9 Watford

10 Bournemouth

ANSWERS

1. Bedfordshire 2. Lancashire 3. Berkshire 4. Kent 5. Devon 6. Somerset
j7. Hampshire 8. Lincolnshire 9. Hertfordshire 10. Dorset

QUIZ 142

. . . .

1. In 1990 who became the youngest man to win the US Open at tennis?

2. What do the initials NFC stand for in the world of American sport?

3. What type of music completes the name of Utah's basketball team?

4. Who were the first baseball team to win five consecutive World Series?

5. How many points is a safety touch worth in American football?

6. In which throwing event did Al Oerter win Olympic gold for the USA?

7. Which US tennis star won his only Wimbledon singles title in 1975?

8. Which was the first US city to host the Summer Olympics?

9. Which Canadian team won baseball's World Series in the 1990s?

10. What B word completes the name of Tampa Bay's American football team?

ANSWERS

1. Pete Sampras 2. National Football Conference 3. Jazz 4. New York Yankees 5. Two 6. Discus 7. Arthur Ashe 8. St Louis 9. Toronto Blue Jays 10. Buccaneers

QUIZ 143

• •

1 In which country is Prestwick golf course?

2 On a dartboard what number is sandwiched by 1 and 4?

3 In which sport do Port Adelaide Power face the Western Bulldogs?

4 What links Hugh Dallas, Jeff Winter and Graham Poll?

5 Which Welsh born boxer of yesteryear was nicknamed the Tonypandy Terror?

6 Which country did Mario Zagallo manage to soccer World Cup glory?

7 What is the duration of the break between rounds in a professional boxing bout?

8 In 2004 who became the first spin bowler to take 500 test wickets?

9 Which Liverpool striker scored his 5th FA Cup final goal in the 1992 final against Sunderland?

10 In which month of the year was the 2004 Aintree Grand National staged?

ANSWERS

1. Scotland 2. 18 3. Australian rules football 4. All soccer referees 5. Tommy Farr 6. Brazil 7. One minute 8. Shane Warne 9. Ian Rush 10. April

QUIZ 144

. . . .

Identify the nicknames of the following football clubs

1 Crystal Palace   The E

2 Northampton Town   The C

3 Bristol Rovers   The P

4 Southampton   The S

5 Port Vale   The V

6 York City   The M

7 Watford   The H

8 Peterborough United The P

9 Aston Villa   The V

10 Grimsby Town   The M

ANSWERS

1. The Eagles 2. The Cobblers 3. The Pirates 4. The Saints 5. The Valiants
6. The Minstermen 7. The Hornets 8. The Posh 9. The Villains 10. The
Mariners

QUIZ 145

1 In horseracing what is sometimes referred to as, the jolly?

2 Which Classic horse race is traditionally contested in the same week as the Epsom Derby?

3 Which RD rode his first Grand National winner on West Tip?

4 The famed steeplechasers Arkle and Foinavon were both named after what?

5 Which course stages the Prix de l'Arc de Triomphe?

6 In 1937, which now annual race was first contested to celebrate the accession of a British monarch?

7 What do the initials PU signify in the form guide of racehorse?

8 Which horse racing course stands on a thoroughfare called St Leger Way?

9 Which race makes up the American Triple Crown with the Kentucky Derby and the Belmont Stakes?

10 In 1953, who won his first Epsom Derby on his 28th and final attempt?

ANSWERS

1. The favourite 2. The Oaks 3. Richard Dunwoody 4. Scottish mountains
5. Longchamps 6. King George VI Stakes 7. Pulled up 8. Doncaster
9. Preakness Stakes 10. Sir Gordon Richards

QUIZ 146

. . . .

1 Who presented South Africa with the 1995 rugby union World Cup trophy?

2 Which US city hosted its first marathon in 1897, a race that has since become an annual event?

3 Which university drew up the first set of offcial rules for association football?

4 Who managed England in the 1986 soccer World Cup finals?

5 Who was the first British driver to record thirty Formula One Grand Prix wins?

6 In which city is the Olympic torch traditionally lit before making its journey to the host city?

7 What colour of running shoes did Michael Johnson wear in the 200m final in the 1996 Olympics?

8 What sport is played by the Anaheim Mighty Ducks?

9 In which city do Lazio FC play their home matches?

10 In 1858, the first Australian rules football club was founded in which Australian city?

ANSWERS

1. Nelson Mandela 2. Boston 3. Cambridge university 4. Bobby Robson
5. Nigel Mansell 6. Olympia 7. Gold 8. Ice hockey 9. Rome 10. Melbourne

QUIZ 147

• •

Which sport links each group of three names?

1 Roy Jones, Chris Byrd, Joe Calzaghe
2 Sean Long, Kris Radlinski, Brett Dallas
3 Tommy Moe, Alberto Tomba, Phil Mahre
4 Reg Harris, Jan Ulrich, Bernard Hinault
5 Padraig Harrington, Lee Westwood, Jumbo Ozaki
6 Brett Ormerod, Ray Parlour, Duncan Ferguson
7 Ted Hankey, Bobby George, Ray Barneveld
8 Jason Weaver, Fred Archer, Kieron Fallon
9 Mark Taylor, Adam Gilchrist, Steve Waugh
10 Greg Hancock, Ivan Mauger, Peter Collins

ANSWERS

QUIZ 148

. . . .

1   In which year did Brazil win their third World Cup?

2   Which German striker won consecutive European Footballer of the Year awards in 1980 and 1981?

3   Who succeeded Jack Charlton as manager of the Republic of Ireland?

4   What is the German counterpart of England's Premiership?

5   Which bird provides the nickname of Brighton FC?

6   Which country co-hosted Euro 2000 with the Netherlands?

7   With which French football club did Eric Cantona win his first league title?

8   Who managed England at Euro 2000?

9   Which star player of the 1966 World Cup finals was nicknamed the Black Panther?

10 Which Scottish football league club has the shortest name?

ANSWERS

1. 1970 2. Karl Heinz-Rummenigge 3. Mick McCarthy 4. Bundesliga
5. Seagulls 6. Belguim 7. Marseilles 8. Kevin Keegan 9. Eusibio 10. Clyde
(not Ayr who are called Ayr United)

QUIZ 149

1 What began at Soldier Field in the city of Chicago on June 17, 1994?

2 Which Swede lifted the Wimbledon title in 1988 and 1990?

3 Which test venue is the home ground of Nottinghamshire CCC?

4 On which Scottish golf course is the famed hole known as the Postage Stamp?

5 A bonspiel is a tournament in which sport?

6 Which British city hosted the 1958 Commonwealth Games?

7 Which colourful horse did Richard Guest ride to victory in the 2001 Grand National?

8 Which Brazilian star striker was voted European Footballer of the Year in 2002?

9 Which US state hosted the 2002 Winter Olympics?

10 Which host nation won the soccer World Cup in 1998?

ANSWERS

1. The 1994 soccer World Cup 2. Stefan Edberg 3. Trent Bridge 4. Troon
5. Curling 6. Cardiff 7. Red Marauder 8. Ronaldo 9. Utah 10. France

QUIZ 150

. . . .

What is the nationality of the …

1   athlete Ingrid Kristiansen?

2   pole vaulter Sergei Bubka?

3   motor racing driver Jacques Villeneuve?

4   golfer Ian Baker-Finch?

5   footballer Stephane Henchoz?

6   cyclist Miguel Indurain?

7   athlete Fanny Blankers-Koen?

8   motor racing legend Juan Manuel Fangio?

9   athlete Paavo Nurmi?

10   boxer Roberto Duran?

ANSWERS

1. Norwegian 2. Ukranian 3. Canadian 4. Australian 5. Swiss 6. Spanish
7. Dutch 8. Argentine 9. Finnish 10. Panamanian

QUIZ 151

• •

Can you pick the correct answer from the three
choices given?

1 Was the boxer Gene Tunney nicknamed the
Fighting Soldier or the Fighting Marine?

2 How many times did Brazil reach the final of the
World Cup in the 20th century, 5, 6 or 7?

3 Is Kempton Park race course located in Middlesex,
Surrey or Essex?

4 Did the sport of orienteering originate in New
Zealand, Canada or Sweden?

5 Which fruit is depicted on the badge of
Worcestershire CCC, a pear, a peach or a
pineapple?

6 What nationality is the tennis star Goran
Ivanisevic, Hungarian, Croatian or Bulgarian?

7 In which European capital did Celtic win the 1967
European Cup final, Lisbon, Rome or Madrid?

8 Was Koroibos, the first ever winner of the marathon
in the ancient Olympics, a baker or a builder?

9 Was the world's first ever golf club founded in
London, Dublin or Edinburgh?

10 Is the Hopman Cup contested in the long jump,
tennis or cricket?

ANSWERS

1. The Fighting Marine 2. Six 3. Middlesex 4. Sweden 5. A pear 6. Croatian
7. Lisbon 8. Baker 9. Edinburgh 10. Tennis

QUIZ 152

• •

1 Was the first FA Cup Final held in: (a) 1868, (b) 1872 or (c) 1876?

2 In which month is the Ascot race meeting held?

3 In motor racing, what is the colour of flag to signify 'Danger, no overtaking': (a) red, (b) blue or (c) yellow?

4 What is the name of the international biennial yachting event coinciding with 'Cowes Week'?

5 How many pieces does each player have in Backgammon?

6 'Boston Crab' is a term used in which sport?

7 What is the name of Chicago's American Football team?

8 How many pegs or marbles are there in a Solitaire board game?

9 The author Dick Francis was formerly famous in which sport?

10 What is the name of Fulham's football ground?

ANSWERS

1. (b) 1872. 2. June. 3. (c) Yellow. 4. 'Admiral's Cup'. 5. 15. 6. Wrestling.
7. 'Bears'. 8. 33. 9. Horse racing. 10. 'Craven Cottage'.

QUIZ 153

. . . .

1 'Seasiders' is the nickname of which football team?

2 Who was declared the winner of the men's 100 metres at the 1988 Olympic Games after Ben Johnson was disqualified?

3 'Albatross' is a term used in which sport?

4 How many pieces are there in a chess game?

5 What is missing from this list of characters from Cluedo: 'Colonel Mustard', 'Professor Plum', 'Reverend Green', 'Miss Scarlet' and 'Mrs White'?

6 'Jib', 'Halyards' and 'Sheets' are terms used in which sport?

7 Is the marathon distance (a) 26 miles 350 yards, (b) 26 miles 375 yards or (c) 26 miles 385 yards?

8 How many balls are there in a game of snooker?

9 In athletics, what is a 'Fosbury Flop'?

10 'The Wightman Cup' is awarded in which sport?

ANSWERS

1. Blackpool. 2. Carl Lewis. 3. Golf. 4. 32. 5. 'Mrs Peacock'. 6. Sailing.
7. (c) 26 miles 385 yards. 8. 21 + cue ball. 9. Backward style of High Jump.
10. Tennis.

QUIZ 154

. . . .

1 Who was the first to score 100 goals in football's Premier League?

2 The Westchester Cup is awarded for which sport?

3 What is another name for the sport of motocross?

4 How many players are there in a Gaelic Football team?

5 What is the highest grade awarded in judo?

6 In which year was the first football World Cup held?

7 On the four Jacks in a pack of standard playing cards, how many eyes appear in total?

8 Which sport was named after the home of the Duke of Beaufort?

9 In which year was Nigel Mansell Formula One World Champion?

10 What is the club song for West Ham United?

ANSWERS

1. Alan Shearer. 2. Polo. 3. Scrambling. 4. 15. 5. 12th dan (white). 6. 1930 (In Uruguay). 7. 12. 8. Badminton. 9. 1992. 10. 'I'm Forever Blowing Bubbles'.

QUIZ 155

. . . .

1 'Old Trafford' is the ground of which football team?

2 In which sport would you use the term 'Dormie'?

3 Which horse won the 'Grand National' in 1973, 1974 and 1977?

4 The term 'Face-off' is used in which sport?

5 Who was America's 'Golden Girl' who fell in the 3,000 metres at the Los Angeles Olympics?

6 In which sport would you find a 'brakeman'?

7 What is the term for dwarf plant growing?

8 Lasse Viren was one of the world's greatest long-distance runners. From which country did he come?

9 With which sport do you associate John and Michael Whittaker?

10 Clive Lloyd captained which national cricket team?

ANSWERS

QUIZ 156

1 In which Olympic Games were women's athletic events included for the first time?

2 Where was the first motor racing Grand Prix held in 1906?

3 Which two sports are played in a biathlon?

4 How long does a hockey match last?

5 In which hobby is the term 'French knot' used?

6 In which year was the London Marathon first held?

7 Who won both the 1989 and 1990 US Masters golf titles?

8 What was the name of the car in which Donald Campbell broke the land-speed record in 1964?

9 Which tennis player appeared in Wimbledon Men's Singles Finals at the ages of 19 and 39?

10 In what year did Mike Tyson beat Trevor Burbick to become Heavyweight World Champion?

ANSWERS

1. 1928 2. Le Mans, France 3. Cross Country Skiing and Rifle Shooting
4. 70 minutes 5. Embroidery 6. 1981 7. Nick Faldo 8. 'Bluebird' 9. Ken Rosewall 10. 1986

QUIZ 157

• •

1 In athletics, how many events are there in a heptathlon?

2 How does a crown-green bowling green differ from an ordinary bowling green?

3 Johnny Weissmuller played the role of 'Tarzan'. Of which sport had he been a champion?

4 What is the name of the rubber disc used in ice hockey?

5 How many strikes per turn are allowed in a game of conkers?

6 What is the name of the ground which is the home of English Rugby Union?

7 The Formula One World Championship began in; (a) 1952, (b) 1950 or (c) 1955?

8 Is the maximum number of clubs that player may use in a round of golf; (a) 12, (b) 13 or (c) 14?

9 During a penalty shoot-out, where should non-participating players be?

10 In which year did the famous cricketer W. G. Grace die?

ANSWERS

1. Seven. 2. It has a hump in the middle, which makes the game more difficult. 3. Swimming. 4. The puck. 5. Three. 6. Twickenham. 7. (b) 1950. 8. 14. 9. In the centre circle. 10. 1915.

QUIZ 158

• •

1. Which English club's football supporters would you associate with the song 'You'll Never Walk Alone'?

2. A game of ice hockey is divided into three periods. How long does each period last?

3. In which game is the term 'Royal Flush' used?

4. How many gold medals did swimmer Mark Spitz win at the Munich Olympic Games in 1972?

5. In rowing, what is the name of the Cambridge University reserve team?

6. Pelé played three times for Brazil in football's World Cup. True or false?

7. How many players are there in a netball team?

8. Who won the 1998 Formula One World Championship?

9. What score do you get if you hit the 'bull's eye' at darts?

10. Which football team is nicknamed 'The Imps'?

ANSWERS

1. Liverpool 2. 20 minutes 3. Poker 4. Seven 5. 'Goldie' 6. False (four times)
7. Seven 8. Mika Hakkinen 9. 50 10. Lincoln City

QUIZ 159

. . . .

1　In Monopoly, with how much money does each player start?

2　Which TV celebrity is on the Board of Directors of Norwich City?

3　What was the original name of 'Bingo'?

4　Who was the captain of the 1966 England World Cup team?

5　In which sport was Betty Calloway a coach?

6　What nationality was the racing driver Emerson Fittipaldi?

7　How many pieces are there in a game of draughts?

8　In diving, the word 'scuba' is made up from the initials of which words?

9　Who sailed single-handedly round the world in 1967?

10　A game of polo is divided into periods. What are they called?

ANSWERS

1. £1,500. 2. Delia Smith. 3. 'Housey-Housey'. 4. Bobby Moore. 5. Ice dance (for Torvill and Dean). 6. Brazilian. 7. 24. 8. Self-Contained Underwater Breathing Apparatus. 9. Francis Chichester. 10. Chukkers (or Chukkas).

QUIZ 160

1 The motorcycle road race held on the Isle of Man is called the TT. What does TT stand for?

2 Who won the UEFA Cup in 1973?

3 On which golf course is the US masters always played?

4 What type of game is euchre?

5 How many players are on each side in a game of polo?

6 In the dice game craps, what number is designated 'snake eyes'?

7 Which American racing driver won the world Grand Prix championship in 1978?

8 Who was the first gymnast to score a perfect 10 in an Olympic gymnastics competition?

9 Which cricketer ended his career with a test batting average of 99.94?

10 What is the game resembling hurling played in the Scottish Highlands?

ANSWERS

1. Tourist Trophy 2. Liverpool. 3. The Augusta National Golf Course. 4. A card game 5. Four 6. Two 7. Mario Andretti. 8. Nadia Comaneci of Romania 9. Don Bradman 10. Shinty

QUIZ 161

· ·

1 How many properties are there on a Monopoly board?

2 Which female US tennis player was known as 'Little Mo'?

3 What are the periods into which a game of polo is divided called?

4 In poker, what is a 'blaze'?

5 Which Australian golfer is known as the 'Great White Shark'?

6 Which game derives its name from the Persian word shah meaning 'a king'?

7 Who is the only world heavyweight boxing champion to retire without ever being defeated?

8 In golf what is an 'albatross'?

9 The footballer Tom Finney played for only one Football League club, his home-town team. What was the club?

10 What is the longest athletics race in the Olympic Games?

ANSWERS

1. 28. 2. Maureen Connolly. 3. Chukkas. 4. A hand containing only court-cards. 5. Greg Norman. 6. Chess. 7. Rocky Marciano. 8. A score of three strokes under par for a hole. 9. Preston North End. 10. The 50km (31.5 miles) walk.

QUIZ 162

. . . .

1   Which cricketer became the first professional captain of the England team in 1953?

2   How many domino tiles are there in a standard set?

3   Which horse won the Grand National in 1973, 1974 and 1977?

4   Who did Muhammad Ali defeat to become the world heavyweight boxing champion in 1964?

5   How is Edson Arantes do Nascimento better known?

6   Who is the only racing driver to win the world championship driving his own car?

7   What is the name of the heroine of the Tomb Raider video games?

8   Where were the Olympic Games held in 1964?

9   Which football club is the object of Nick Hornby's obsession in his book Fever Pitch?

10 Which US golfer was known as 'the Golden Bear'?

ANSWERS

1. Len Hutton 2. 28 3. Red Rum 4. Sonny Liston 5. Pelé 6. Jack Brabham, driving his Repco-Brabham in 1966 7. Lara Croft. 8. Tokyo, Japan
9. Arsenal 10. Jack Nicklaus

QUIZ 163

1. Which boxer was world heavyweight champion between 1937 and 1949?

2. How many holes does a cribbage board have?

3. In baseball, what is a 'switch-hitter'?

4. Who did Bobby Fischer defeat in the world chess championship in 1972?

5. What was burned in 1883 to produce 'The Ashes', kept in an urn, for which the England and Australia cricket teams regularly compete?

6. In which game are various parts of the playing areas called 'penthouse', 'dedan' and 'tambour'?

7. Which athlete won four gold medals at the 1936 Berlin Olympics?

8. Who was the British snooker player who won the world championship fifteen times between 1927 and 1946?

9. What is the name of the blue piece in the game of Cluedo?

10. What is the name of the golf tournament played between teams of male amateurs representing the US and Great Britain and Ireland?

ANSWERS

1. Joe Louis. 2. 120 – four rows of 30 holes each. 3. A batter who can bat either right-handed or left-handed. 4. Boris Spassky. 5. A bail. 6. Real tennis. 7. Jesse Owens. 8. Joe Davis. 9. Mrs Peacock. 10. The Walker Cup.

QUIZ 164

• •

1 Geoff Hurst scored a hat-trick for England in the 1966 World Cup final. Who scored England's other goal?

2 In card games such as solo whist, what does 'misère' mean?

3 What nationality was the racing driver Ayrton Senna?

4 What game was invented by Charles Darrow in 1929, the year of the Wall Street crash?

5 In ice hockey, what is the name of the end-of-season playoff tournament between the top Canadian and US teams?

6 Who were the first British football club to win the European Cup?

7 Which Olympic champion was known as the 'Flying Finn'?

8 Tennis's Grand Slam is made up of Wimbledon, the US Open, the French Open and which other tournament?

9 Which sport features snatches and clean jerks?

10 In what city did Roger Bannister run the first four-minute mile?

ANSWERS

1. Martin Peters. 2. A declaration that a player will win no tricks in a hand.
3. Brazilian. 4. Monopoly. 5. The Stanley Cup. 6. Celtic. 7. Paavo Nurmi.
8. The Australian Open. 9. Weightlifting. 10. Oxford.

QUIZ 165

1 Which swimmer won seven gold medals at the 1972 Olympic Games?

2 In card games, what is a 'prial'?

3 How many different colours are the spaces on a Scrabble board?

4 What sporting event takes place between Putney and Mortlake?

5 In which sport was Jahangir Khan a dominant figure in the 1980s?

6 Who was the first European Footballer of the Year, in 1956?

7 Of which sport are glima, kushti and schwingen all forms?

8 In what year were the Winter Olympics first held?

9 On which US city was the game of Monopoly originally based?

10 Which football club plays at The Dell?

ANSWERS

1. Mark Spitz. 2. Three cards of the same rank in a hand. 3. Five. 4. The Oxford– Cambridge boat race. 5. Squash. 6. Stanley Matthews. 7. Wrestling. 8. 1924. 9. Atlantic City. 10. Southampton.

QUIZ 166

. . . .

1 With which sports are Wayne Gretzky and Gordie Howe associated?

2 According to the rules of cricket, how many forms of dismissal are there?

3 Why was the Italian athlete Dorando Pietri disqualified from the marathon in the 1908 Olympics?

4 Who became Britain's first one million pounds footballer in 1979?

5 What is the name of the Dallas American football team?

6 What have these five sports in common: cycling, fencing, gymnastics, swimming and track and field athletics?

7 Which football team do the 'Toon Army' support?

8 Which playing card is the symbol of love?

9 Who was said to 'float like a butterfly, sting like a bee'?

10 In American football, how many points does a touchdown score?

ANSWERS

1. Ice Hockey. 2. Ten. 3. He had to be assisted by officials on the last lap of the track. 4. Trevor Francis. 5. The Dallas Cowboys. 6. They are the only sports to appear in every modern Olympic Games since 1896. 7. Newcastle United. 8. The nine of hearts. 9. Muhammad Ali. 10. Six.

QUIZ 167

• •

1 In which year was the first Soccer World Cup competition organized?

2 In which sport is the Stanley Cup played for?

3 The longest golf hole in the world is the seventh of Satsuki GU, Sano, Japan, which measures 964 yards/881 metres. What par is it?

4 How many gold medals did swimmer Mark Spitz win at the 1972 Olympics?

5 How many runs did Victoria score in 10.5 hours in a cricket match against New South Wales in 1926?

6 Who was the shamed 1987 World 100 metre sprint champion?

7 How many players are in a male lacrosse team?

8 How many times has Jaques Anquetil won the Tour de France?

9 How long does the Le Mans Motor Race last for?

10 Who is the most successful tennis player in the history of the game (male or female)?

ANSWERS

1. 1930. 2. Ice hockey. 3. Par seven. 4. Seven. 5. 1,107 runs. 6. Ben Johnson.
7. Ten. 8. Five. 9. 24 hours. 10. Martina Navratilova.

QUIZ 168

. . . .

1   In which Scottish town do the two top football teams have grounds on the same street, 100 yards apart?

2   How many players are playing in a team of Australian Rules football at any one time.

3   What is the maximum number of clubs a golfer may carry during a round of Golf?

4   Which Scottish sprinter won Gold in the 100 metres in Moscow, 1980?

5   Which Warwickshire batsman, scored the following successive scores in 1994: 147/106/120 not out /136/26/140/501 not out?

6   In athletics, which track race is called the Metric Mile?

7   Who won nine Gold Medals for swimming during the 1968 and 1972 Olympics?

8   What is the shortest distance raced, in cycling, on the track in the Olympics?

9   Silverstone, Aintree, Brooklands and Donnington have all been used for Formula 1. Which other British circuit was also used?

10 In which town are the oldest surviving 'real' tennis courts, built in 1539 in a Scottish palace grounds?

ANSWERS

1. Dundee. 2. 18. 3. 14. 4. Alan Wells. 5. Brian Lara. 6. 1,500 metres.
7. Mark Spitz. 8. 1,000 metre sprint. 9. Brands Hatch. 10. Falkirk

QUIZ 169

1. Spurs lost against Chelsea three-two on 1 December 1990 and were fined for being late. Why?

2. In American football how many teams does each side have at a match?

3. What is the Ryder Cup?

4. Who was the first European Olympic Champion who won the 100m in 1924 and was immortalized in the film Chariots of Fire?

5. Which cricketer made 18 centuries in 50 innings in 1947?

6. The Athlete Sergey Bubka dominated which Field event in the 1980s and 1990s?

7. How many players play at any one time in a water polo team?

8. How many one-day stages does the Tour de France have?

9. When was the last Grand Prix held in the USA?

10. In table tennis, how many points (minimum) must you score to win a game?

ANSWERS

1. Team coach was towed away. 2. Three teams (Offensive/Defensive/Special or Kicking). 3. USA v Europe, biennial golf tournament. 4. Harold Abrahams. 5. Denis Compton. 6. Pole Vault. 7. Seven players. 8. 21 stages. 9. 1991. 10. 21 points.

QUIZ 170

. . . .

1 How many seconds did it take Vinny Jones to be booked in his match on 19 January 1991?

2 Michael Jordan played basketball for whom?

3 Who has finished highest in the European 'Order of Merit' Golf Tour for six consecutive years?

4 British Women Heptathlon champion, Denise Lewis, competes in how many events to make up the Heptathlon?

5 Ian Botham made 5,200 runs in 102 test matches but how many catches did he make?

6 How many Gold Medals did Daley Thompson win at the Olympics?

7 Which sport would you be performing if you were doing a 'ballet leg double', a 'knight' or 'castle', a 'tuck', a 'front pike' or a 'split'?

8 How many 'Chukkers' make up a game of polo?

9 In a career of ten years in Formula One, which driver achieved pole position in over 40% of races entered and won one in every four?

10 Which squash player was not defeated between 1981 and 1986?

ANSWERS

1. Five seconds. 2. Chicago Bulls. 3. Colin Montgomerie. 4. Seven. 5. 120.
6. Two. 7. Synchronized swimming. 8. Six. 9. Ayrton Senna. 10. Jahangir Khan.

QUIZ 171

1 Which football club were the first in Great Britain to introduce a stripe down the seam of their shorts?

2 Which baseball team play in New York?

3 The oldest golf player to score his age was Arthur Thompson in 1973. How old was he?

4 What is the longest race in men's athletics?

5 Who took 434 wickets in 131 Tests by early 1994?

6 Over what distance are the men's athletics High Hurdles?

7 What is the length of an Olympic size swimming pool?

8 Where is the oldest annually contested motorcycle race held?

9 How many laps is the Indianapolis 500?

10 Who became the youngest ever international footballer to play for Wales?

ANSWERS

1. Everton. 2. Yankies. 3. 103 years old. 4. 50 km (31 miles) walk. 5. Kapil Dev. 6. 110m (120yds). 7. 50m (54.5yds). 8. The Isle of Man. 9. 200. 10. Ryan Giggs.

QUIZ 172

1 How many games did it take Jimmy Greaves to score his 351st goal?

2 What sport is Wayne Gretzky famous for?

3 How many golf courses are there at St Andrew's on the Links?

4 There are two courses at Newmarket. One is the Rowley mile, what is the other one called?

5 How many times did Wilfred Rhodes complete the 'Cricket Double' of 1,000 runs and 100 wickets in a season between 1903 and 1926?

6 Who set six world records for athletics within 45 minutes on 25 August 1935 in Michigan, USA?

7 How many dives is the men's Olympic high board diving scored out of?

8 What sport was Greg Le Mond famous for?

9 The 'Network Q' Rally of Great Britain was formerly sponsored by whom?

10 Two British men finished in the top ten of the ATP World Tennis Rankings at the end of 1998. One was Tim Henman, who was the other?

ANSWERS

1. 500. 2. Ice Hockey. 3. Four (Old/New/Eden/Jubilee). 4. The July Course. 5. 16. 6. Jesse Owens. 7. Ten. 8. Cycling. 9. RAC. 10 Greg Rusedski.

QUIZ 173

• •

1 Why did Doncaster Rovers' goalkeeper, Ken Hardwick, not get to play in the England Under 23's trial in January 1955 after being asked to?

2 Which Pro American football team play in San Francisco?

3 Sam Snead recorded the lowest score ever for 36 holes in 1959. What was his score?

4 Women's gymnastics is made up of Vault, Floor, Uneven Bars and what other event?

5 In 1990 at Victoria, Australian cricketer Gary Chapman scored a record number of runs from one ball with no overthrows. What was his score?

6 In which city was the first Athletics World Championship held in 1983?

7 How many strokes would you do if you swam in the Individual Medley Race?

8 There are three weapons used in fencing: the Foil, the Épée and which other?

9 Who won the Formula 1 Grand Prix from Nigel Mansell by 0.014 seconds in Spain on 13 April 1986?

10 Which famous tennis player now hosts A Question of Sport?

ANSWERS

1. He was 30 years old! 2. Forty Niners. 3. 122. 4. Beam. 5. 17. 6. Helsinki.
7. Four. 8. Saber. 9. Ayrton Senna. 10. Sue Barker.

QUIZ 174

. . . .

1. Who won the 1970 football World Cup Final?

2. What is the name of the Dallas American football team?

3. Kriss Akabusi moved from running the 400m to competing in what event?

4. What sport do the New York Mets play?

5. How wide is a basketball court?

6. What is the name of the world governing body of football?

7. Which woman won the Wimbledon singles title in 1981?

8. What golf shot is John Daly famous for?

9. What is the name of Chelsea Football Club's ground?

10. In cricket what does LBW stand for?

ANSWERS

1. Brazil. 2. Dallas Cowboys. 3. 400m hurdles. 4. Baseball. 5. 14 metres (46 feet). 6. FIFA (Fédération Internationale de Football Association). 7. Chris Evert-Lloyd. 8. Long drives (tee shots). 9. Stamford Bridge. 10. Leg Before Wicket.

QUIZ 175

1 Who missed the final penalty for England in the 1990 World Cup semi-final?

2 What is the name of the main trophy in American football?

3 Backley and Hill compete for Great Britain in which sport?

4 Kristen Otto won six gold medals in the 1988 Olympic Games, but in what sport?

5 What is the real name of 'Dickie' Bird?

6 How many Formula 1 World Championships did Jackie Stewart win?

7 Angus Fraser is famous for playing what sport?

8 One hundred and ten feet is the longest putt ever holed. Two people have achieved it. Nick Price is one, who is the other?

9 Arthur Ashe is famous for which sport?

10 Which basketball player starred alongside cartoon characters in the film Space Jam?

ANSWERS

1. Chris Waddle. 2. Super Bowl. 3. Javelin. 4. Swimming. 5. Harold Bird.
6. Three. 7. Cricket. 8. Jack Nicklaus. 9. Tennis. 10. Michael Jordan.

QUIZ 176

. . . .

1 In which country was the 1982 football World Cup held?

2 Complete the name of the American football team 'The Washington…'?

3 What nationality is the former 2000m and 5000m world record holder Said Aouita?

4 Who trained Corbiere, the winner of the 1983 Grand National?

5 If you were watching the football team River Plate, what country would you be in?

6 How many basketball players, from one team, are allowed on court at any one time?

7 Where is the American Open Tennis Championships held?

8 Shaq and Magic are associated with which sport?

9 The Buccaneers, Cowboys and Steelers all play what sport?

10 Who won the 1970 FA Cup Final?

ANSWERS

1. Spain. 2. Redskins. 3. Moroccan. 4. Jenny Pitman. 5. Argentina. 6. Five.
7. Flushing Meadows, New York. 8. Baseball. 9. American Football.
10. Chelsea.

QUIZ 177

1 In what sport were Flach and Seguso a famous partnership?

2 What country did Niki Lauda drive for?

3 In which year was the Football Association founded?

4 Sergi Bubka is famous for competing in what sporting event?

5 What is the name given to the player who throws the ball in American football?

6 Who are the 'Toffee Men' in football?

7 How many players do you find in a baseball team?

8 What do the initials TCCB stand for?

9 What country won the first Rugby Union World Cup?

10 Who was the top scorer in the 1982 football World Cup Final?

ANSWERS

1. Tennis. 2. Austria. 3. 1863. 4. Pole vault. 5. The Quarterback. 6. Everton.
7. Nine. 8. Test and County Cricket Board. 9. New Zealand. 10. Paulo Rossi.

QUIZ 178

. . . .

1 In which year was the Ryder Cup established?

2 Which German has won the football World Cup as both a player and a manager?

3 'The Refrigerator' is famous for playing which sport?

4 What is the main trophy in American baseball?

5 Who partnered Martina Navratilova to four successive women's doubles championships at Wimbledon?

6 Who scored the last goal for France in the 1998 football World Cup Final?

7 Daley Thompson is famous for competing in which athletics event?

8 In which country would you watch Indy Car Racing?

9 Who became the youngest Formula One Racing Champion in 1972?

10 Complete the boxer's name 'Marvellous Marvin…'?

ANSWERS

1. 1927. 2. Franz Beckenbauer. 3. American Football. 4. The World Series.
5. Pam Shriver. 6. Emmanuel Petit. 7. The Decathlon. 8. USA. 9. Emerson
Fittipaldi. 10. Hagler.

QUIZ 179

• •

1 Who knocked England out of the 1986 Football World Cup Finals?

2 What animal do you associate with the Chicago American Football team?

3 When did Steffi Graf win her first Wimbledon singles title?

4 In what sport did Ingrid Kristiansen hold three world records during 1989?

5 What country does golfer Vijay Singh come from?

6 When was FIFA, the governing body of football, formed?

7 Who was Ayrton Senna's team mate for McLaren in 1990?

8 What is the official height of cricket stumps?

9 Where in America are the famous Dodgers baseball team from?

10 With which sport do you associate former World Champion Neil Adams?

ANSWERS

1. Argentina. 2. Bears. 3. 1988. 4. Athletics (5,000m, 10,000m and the marathon). 5. Fiji. 6. 1904. 7. Gerhard Berger. 8. 26 inches (71.1 cm). 9. Los Angeles. 10. Judo.

QUIZ 180

• •

1 Who was John McEnroe's partner in an extremely successful tennis doubles team?

2 At what football ground do Blackpool play?

3 What country does athlete Colin Jackson come from?

4 Who are the Lakers in American basketball?

5 Trevino, Player and Nicklaus are legends in what sport?

6 Which country won the 1988 European Football Championships?

7 How many players from one team are allowed on the field of play, at any one time, in a game of American football?

8 For which team did Damon Hill race in 1998?

9 What is the name for the piece of wood that rests on top of a set of cricket stumps?

10 Who won the Tour de France in 1987?

ANSWERS

1. Peter Fleming. 2. Bloomfield Park. 3. Wales. 4. Los Angeles Lakers. 5. Golf.
6. Holland. 7. 11 (12 in Canada). 8. Jordan. 9. The bails. 10. Stephen Roche.

QUIZ 181

. . . .

1 Who is the voice of BBC Golf?

2 Which country reached the 1974 and 1978 football World Cup Finals, but ended up runners up in both?

3 Denise Lewis competes for Great Britain in which athletic event?

4 On 28 January 1996, what sporting event was watched by over eight hundred million people world wide?

5 At which cricket ground would you find the Nursery End?

6 Who was the youngest woman to win the Wimbledon singles title beating Lottie Dod's record by a matter of days?

7 What sports company named a range of trainer after basketball legend Michael Jordan?

8 Black Jack and Stud Poker are what type of game?

9 Who was the manager of the England football team in the 1990 World Cup?

10 What shape are your skis in if you are 'snowploughing'?

ANSWERS

1. Peter Alliss. 2. Holland. 3. The Heptathlon. 4. The Super Bowl. 5. Lords.
6. Martina Hingis. 7. Nike (Nike Air Jordan). 8. Card games. 9. Bobby Robson.
10. A 'V' shape.

QUIZ 182

. . . .

1   What sport does Laura Davies play?

2   'Gully', 'silly point' and 'third man' are all positions in which sport?

3   What is the name of Bristol City Football Club's home ground?

4   Who was the first unseeded player to win the men's singles title at Wimbledon?

5   If you were being trained by Emanuel Steward, what sport would you be competing in?

6   How many players are there on each side in a game of Olympic beach volleyball?

7   Where does the hooker stand for a scrum in Rugby Union?

8   Sensini, Roa and Veron played for what team in the 1998 Football World Cup?

9   How many times does an athlete have to run round an Olympic track in an 800 metre race?

10 In which year was table tennis made an Olympic sport?

ANSWERS

1. Golf. 2. Cricket. 3. Ashton Gate. 4. Boris Becker. 5. Boxing. 6. Two.
7. In the middle of the front row. 8. Argentina. 9. Twice. 10. 1988.

QUIZ 183

• •

1. If you were at the Augusta National Club, what sport would you be watching?

2. Who did cricketer Graham Gooch score 333 runs against in 1990?

3. Has Ivan Lendl ever won Wimbledon?

4. Who was the captain of England's football team that won the World Cup in 1966?

5. With what racing team did James Hunt win the Formula 1 World Championship?

6. How many points do you need in chess to become a 'Grand Master'?

7. What does the word Karate mean?

8. Who did Everton beat in the 1984 FA Cup Final?

9. In 1990, the San Francisco 49ers achieved the highest score ever in a Super Bowl. Who was it against?

10. Who won three Olympic long jump gold medals in a row?

ANSWERS

1. Golf. 2. India. 3. No. 4. Bobby Moore. 5. McLaren. 6. 2,500 points.
7. Empty hand. 8. Watford. 9. Denver Broncos. 10. Carl Lewis.

QUIZ 184

1 If you were watching the 'Addicks', what football team would you be watching?

2 When did Alain Prost retire from competing in Formula 1 racing?

3 Can a catch in cricket be taken after hitting only the glove of the batsman?

4 Fanny Sunsesson was the well known caddie for what golfer?

5 How many times have Italy won the football World Cup?

6 In what year did Linford Christie win the 100 metres Olympic gold medal?

7 Who recorded the fastest tennis serve by hitting the ball at 149 mph in March 1998?

8 How many games did American football's Tampa Bay Buccaneers lose in a row during the season 1976–77?

9 What team did Robbie Earle play for in the 1998 Football World Cup Final?

10 Who won the Formula 1 World Title in 1982?

ANSWERS

1. Charlton Athletic FC. 2. 1993. 3. Yes. 4. Nick Faldo. 5. Three times. 6. 1991. 7. Greg Rusedski. 8. 26 games. 9. Jamaica. 10. Keke Rosberg.

QUIZ 185

. . . .

1 Who is the chairman of Leyton Orient Football Club?

2 If a cricket umpire holds both arms straight up in the air, what is he indicating?

3 How many times in the 1980s did Severiano Ballesteros win the US Masters Golf?

4 If you were at Goodwood, what sport would you be watching?

5 When was the first Rugby Union World Cup held?

6 Who won the 1900 FA Cup Final?

7 How many times did Chuck Noll win the Super Bowl as the manager of the Pittsburgh Steelers?

8 If you were receiving a coaching lesson from David Leadbetter, what sport would you be attempting to play?

9 As well as Chris Waddle, who was the other player to miss a penalty in the 1990 football World Cup semi final?

10 What is the name of Damon Hill's famous father?

ANSWERS

1. Barry Hearn. 2. Six runs scored. 3. Twice (1980 and 1983). 4. Horse racing.
5. 1987. 6. Bury. 7. Four times. 8. Golf. 9. Stuart Pearce. 10. Graham Hill.

QUIZ 186

. . . .

1 What sport do Roger Clements and Pedro Martinez play?

2 What is the height of a badminton net?

3 Who won the 1976–77 Le Mans race in France?

4 What international team did footballer Vinny Jones captain?

5 What sport is played at Wentworth, Sunningdale and Turnberry?

6 With which Formula 1 team do you associate Ron Dennis?

7 How many Wimbledon titles did Billie Jean King win between 1961 and 1979?

8 Between both teams, how many times have the San Francisco 49ers and the Dallas Cowboys won the Super Bowl (until 1998)?

9 Who won the FA Cup in 1968?

10 What implement do competitors pass on in a relay race?

ANSWERS

1. Baseball. 2. One and a half metres (five feet). 3. Porsche. 4. Wales. 5. Golf.
6. McLaren. 7. Twenty. 8. Ten. 9. West Bromwich Albion. 10. A baton.

QUIZ 187

1 For which country does footballer George Weah play?

2 In what sport do you use woods and irons?

3 Gerald McCellan beat Jay Bell in a world title fight during 1993. How many seconds did it last?

4 What country does sprinter Frankie Fredricks come from?

5 In Rugby it is called a try. What is the equivalent in American football?

6 Who is the third highest test wicket taker in history?

7 When did indoor volleyball become an Olympic sport?

8 Who won the FA Cup in 1961 and 1962?

9 When did Martina Navratilova win her final women's singles title at Wimbledon?

10 At what football club did Gary Lineker begin his football career?

ANSWERS

1. Liberia. 2. Golf. 3. Twenty seconds. 4. Namibia. 5. A touchdown.
6. Courtney Walsh. 7. 1964. 8. Tottenham Hotspur. 9. 1990. 10. Leicester City.

QUIZ 188

• •

1 Who was the most expensive footballer in the Brazilian squad for the 1998 Football World Cup?

2 In 1991, who was the non playing captain of the European Ryder Cup team?

3 WBA and WBC are governing bodies in what sport?

4 Which country holds the most Davis Cup tennis titles?

5 Cricketer Salim Malik scored 215 runs in an innings for Essex in 1991. Who was it against?

6 Who was the top scorer in the 1966 football World Cup Final?

7 Where were the 1988 Olympic Games held?

8 In what year did Michael Schumacher win his first Formula One World Championship?

9 What sport do Neath and Llanelli play?

10 How tall are the hurdles in a 110m hurdles race?

ANSWERS

1. Denilson. 2. Bernard Gallacher. 3. Boxing. 4. USA. 5. Leicestershire.
6. Eusebio. 7. Seoul, Korea. 8. 1994. 9. Rugby Union. 10. 106.7 cm (3 feet 6 inches).

QUIZ 189

1 Who won the first Johnnie Walker Golf World Championship in 1991?

2 Peter Schmeichel won the football European Championships with which country?

3 What sport does Lee Janzen play?

4 Who launched the new McLaren car for season 1997?

5 What colour rose do your associate with Lancashire Cricket Club?

6 From what football club did Arsenal buy Ian Wright?

7 What English tennis player was disqualified from a doubles match at Wimbledon for hitting a ball girl with a ball?

8 In which year did Steve Ovett win an Olympic gold medal in the 800 metres?

9 There are two major leagues in American baseball, one is the American League. What is the other?

10 How many players are there per team in an Australian Rules football match?

ANSWERS

1. Fred Couples. 2. Denmark. 3. Golf. 4. The Spice Girls. 5. Red. 6. Crystal Palace. 7. Tim Henman. 8. 1980. 9. National League. 10. 18 a side.

QUIZ 190

1 Which current Premier Football manager was nicknamed the 'Stroller' when he played football?

2 What country does golfer Bernhard Langer come from?

3 Who trained both Muhammad Ali and Sugar Ray Leonard?

4 Where do Barnsley Football Club play?

5 Who became Michael Schumacher's team mate at Ferrari in 1996?

6 What letter in the alphabet are the goal posts in rugby shaped like?

7 How many races did Desert Orchid win out of the 55 jump races that he started?

8 In what sport would you do a 'lay up shot'?

9 How many points do you get for a touch down in American football?

10 Where was tennis player Anna Kournikova born?

ANSWERS

1. George Graham. 2. Germany. 3. Angelo Dundee. 4. Oakwell. 5. Eddie Irvine. 6. An 'H'. 7. 27. 8. Basketball. 9. Six points. 10. Moscow, Russia.

QUIZ 191

. . . .

1 Which country did Dino Zoff famously play football for?

2 What sport is Jonah Lomu famous for?

3 Old Trafford is the headquarters for which cricket team?

4 Who became the youngest ever scorer in the football World Cup in 1998?

5 Which man won 12 Grand Slam tennis titles between 1961 and 1967?

6 Whose record of four gold medals in Olympic track and field did Carl Lewis equal in 1984?

7 Joe DiMaggio played 56 consecutive baseball games for which team?

8 When was the Australian Football Council formed?

9 How many pole positions did the late Ayrton Senna win?

10 What sport do you associate with the Harlem Globetrotters with?

ANSWERS

1. Italy. 2. Rugby Union. 3. Lancashire. 4. Michael Owen. 5. Roy Emerson.
6. Jesse Owens. 7. New York Yankees. 8. 1906. 9. 65. 10. Basketball.

QUIZ 192

• •

1 In what sport do you score by dunking a ball?

2 Which ex-Liverpool player was Kevin Keegan's right hand man at Newcastle United?

3 Moses Kiptanui was the first man to run the 3,000 metres under how many minutes?

4 How many Grand Slam tournaments did Margaret Court achieve in her career?

5 Who is Alexander Lyle better known as?

6 What animal do you associate with Leicester City?

7 Grace Road is the home of what cricket club?

8 How many Grand Prix did Jonny Herbert win in 1995?

9 Who won the 1986 Snooker World Championships?

10 Who is the oldest player to ever play in the football World Cup Finals?

ANSWERS

1. Basketball. 2. Terry McDermott. 3. Eight minutes. 4. 24 times. 5. Sandy Lyle. 6. Foxes. 7. Leicestershire. 8. Two. 9. Joe Johnson. 10. Roger Milla.

QUIZ 193

. . . .

1 Which footballer became the most expensive defender in the world in May 1998?

2 Who set the 100 metres World Record in Atlanta during 1996?

3 On what surface is the French Open Tennis Championship held?

4 Name the Glasgow born golfer who turned professional in 1987?

5 Trent Bridge is home to which cricket club?

6 How many times did Alain Prost win the Formula One World Championships?

7 Who was the English footballer that scored a goal against France in 27 seconds?

8 How many points do you get for potting a pink in snooker?

9 For which sport are Freddie Spencer and Barry Sheene famous?

10 Which song did Glenn Hoddle and Chris Waddle release into the UK Top 40?

ANSWERS

1. Jaap Stam. 2. Donovan Bailey. 3. Clay. 4. Colin Montgomerie.
5. Nottinghamshire. 6. Four. 7. Bryan Robson. 8. Six. 9. Motor cycling.
10. 'Diamond Lights'.

QUIZ 194

• •

1 If you were in the Maracana Municipal Stadium what sport would you be watching?

2 What country does sprinter Merlene Ottey come from?

3 Who won the 1993 Golf Open Championship?

4 In what sport does David Coulthard compete?

5 If you are a man between 70kg (154lbs) and 74kg (163lbs), what weight category would you be in for karate?

6 Which was the richest football club in the world in 1998?

7 What country is legendary cricketer Sir Donald Bradman from?

8 If you take a shot in basketball from 22 feet away from the basket, how many points do you get?

9 When did Pat Rafter win the US Open Tennis Championships?

10 Anatoly Karpov and Jan Timman play what game?

ANSWERS

1. Football. 2. Jamaica. 3. Greg Norman. 4. Formula 1 Racing.
5. Middleweight. 6. Manchester United. 7. Australia. 8. Three. 9. 1997.
10. Chess.

QUIZ 195

• •

1 Abel Resino holds the record for the longest period without conceding a goal. What Spanish football team was he playing for when he achieved it?

2 Björn Borg won Wimbledon five times. How many times did he win the French Open?

3 If you were at Waimea Bay, Hawaii, what sport would you be watching?

4 What is the distance between the two uprights on a Rugby goal?

5 Who scored the winning goal in the 1991 FA Cup Final?

6 Which man won 122 consecutive 400-metre hurdles races over a period of ten years?

7 Who was Michael Spinks' boxing brother who also won the Heavyweight World Championship?

8 In what county is the race course Kempton Park?

9 At which golf course did Nick Faldo win the 1987 and 1992 Open Championships?

10 In which South American country did William Weiler send 20 players off in a match?

ANSWERS

1. Athletico Madrid. 2. Six times. 3. Surfing. 4. 5.6 metres. 5. Des Walker.
6. Edwin Moses. 7. Leon Spinks. 8. Middlesex. 9. Muirfield. 10. Paraguay.

QUIZ 196

- -

1 How many points do you get for a conversion in Rugby Union?

2 What sport evolved from the Polynesian practice of standing on canoes?

3 Where did Arsenal sign England International David Seaman from?

4 When were the women's singles added to the All England Tennis Championship?

5 Kingdom and Jackson were great rivals in what sporting event?

6 Who was the manager of Coventry City before Gordon Strachan?

7 Where is the Grand National held every year?

8 In what sport would you find a governing body called the PGA?

9 What cricket club do you associate with Geoffrey Boycott?

10 What does a yellow and red striped flag mean in Formula 1 racing?

ANSWERS

1. Two points. 2. Surfing. 3. Queens Park Rangers. 4. 1884. 5. 110 metre hurdles. 6. Ron Atkinson. 7. Aintree. 8. Golf. 9. Yorkshire. 10 Slippery track.

QUIZ 197

. . . .

1 How many years are there between Jimmy Connors' first win at Wimbledon and his last?

2 What country is famous golfer Gary Player from?

3 How many test matches did John Agnew play for England at cricket?

4 On what Formula 1 track do you find Copse Corner?

5 Who won the 1988 FA Cup Final?

6 In what athletic event did Emma George break the indoor and outdoor world record within the space of a week?

7 In what sport would you find Tony Allcock competing?

8 How many points do you get for a field goal in American football?

9 Who was the first foreign footballer (outside the UK) to captain a winning FA Cup side?

10 When did boxing become legal in Great Britain?

ANSWERS

1. Eight years. 2. South Africa. 3. Three. 4. Silverstone. 5. Wimbledon FC.
6. Pole vault. 7. Bowls. 8. Three points. 9. Eric Cantona. 10. 1901.

QUIZ 198

• •

1 Who scored the winning goal in the 1987 FA Cup Final?

2 What athlete broke six world records in the space of 45 minutes?

3 What country does footballer Zinedine Zidane come from?

4 Who is tennis player Andre Agassi married to?

5 What is the name of the Cup in which female American professional golfers play against those from Europe?

6 Who won the 1995 Cricket World Cup?

7 On what circuit is the German Grand Prix held?

8 How many times did Liverpool win the FA Cup in the 1980s?

9 In what game do you have guards, centres and forwards?

10 What is the name of the Buffalo American football team?

ANSWERS

1. Gary Mabbutt. 2. Jesse Owens. 3. France. 4. Actress Brooke Shields.
5. Solheim Cup. 6. Sri Lanka. 7. Hockenheim. 8. Twice. 9. Basketball.
10. Buffalo Bill.

QUIZ 199

• •

1 Who won the 1980 FA Cup Final?

2 What does 'scratch' mean in golfing terms?

3 Clive Lloyd was the cricket captain of which country?

4 Who won the 1997 Formula 1 Constructors' Championship?

5 What club did Glenn Hoddle manage before he became the coach of the England national team?

6 If you are a Sixth Dan in Judo, what colour belt would you have?

7 Which Williams test driver became a Formula 1 World Champion?

8 Which football club did Chelsea sign Gian Luca Vialli from?

9 With which sport do you associate Vitus Gerulaitus?

10 What is the name given to the 'up and under' which is named after a famous Irish club?

ANSWERS

1. West Ham United. 2. No handicap (zero). 3. West Indies. 4. Williams Renault. 5. Chelsea. 6. Red and white belt. 7. Damon Hill. 8. Juventus. 9. Tennis. 10. Garryowen.

QUIZ 200

• •

1 Who did Aston Villa beat in the Coca Cola Cup Final in season 1996/97?

2 In Britain, what is the term used for a score of three under par on a hole in golf?

3 In what year was the first women's cricket World Cup?

4 The A1 Ring is the home of what Formula 1 Grand Prix?

5 Jonathan Edwards and Willie Banks are famous for what sporting event?

6 Who are the Celtics in American football?

7 Who is Sheffield's Boxing Prince?

8 How many spiked points are there on a Backgammon board?

9 Who replaced Gary Lineker as a substitute in what turned out to be Lineker's final match for England?

10 What animal do you associate with the touring British Isles Rugby Union touring team?

ANSWERS

1. Leeds United. 2. An albatross. 3. 1988. 4. Austrian. 5. Triple Jump.
6. Boston Celtics. 7. Prince Naseem Hamed. 8. 24. 9. Alan Smith. 10. The lion.

QUIZ 201

. . . .

1　What is the name of Derby County's former ground?

2　If you have the 'Yips' in golf, what do you have?

3　In what year did Michael Atherton become the England cricket captain?

4　What colour flag is held out to warn of dangerous conditions on a Formula 1 racing track?

5　Willie Wood and Peter Belliss are famous for what game?

6　When a Quarter Back is tackled or put down in American football, what is this called?

7　'Posh' is the nickname of which football club?

8　In which year did Virginia Wade win the women's Wimbledon singles title?

9　Which Premiership football club did Nigel Winterburn, Dennis Wise and Dave Beasant all play for at one time?

10　In football they are called assistant referees, what are they called in Rugby?

ANSWERS

1. The Baseball Ground. 2. A nervous twitch which inhibits putting. 3. 1993.
4. Yellow Flag. 5. Bowls. 6. Sacked. 7. Peterborough. 8. 1977. 9. Wimbledon.
10. Touch Judges.

QUIZ 202

• •

1 In what sport does Heinz Harald Frentzen compete?

2 Who missed a penalty in the 1988 FA Cup Final?

3 Who was the captain of the winning team in the 1987 Cricket World Cup Final?

4 What is a 'one wood' better known as in golf?

5 Who was the manager of Charlton Athletic in season 1998/99?

6 Robin Cousins is famous for which sport?

7 Where do the Ireland Rugby Union team play their home games?

8 Did John Francome ever win the Grand National?

9 Which Premiership football team were formerly called the 'Thames Ironworks FC'?

10 Can a Goal Attack score in a game of netball?

ANSWERS

1. Formula 1. 2. John Aldridge. 3. Allan Border. 4. A Driver. 5. Alan Curbishley. 6. Figure Skating. 7. Lansdowne Road. 8. No. 9. West Ham United. 10. Yes.

QUIZ 203

- -

1 Who became the oldest player to play in the NBA in April 1997?

2 Newton Heath became which world famous football club?

3 Is the Walker Cup golf competition for amateurs or professionals?

4 When was the first Cricket World Cup?

5 Renaldo Nehemiah was famous for which athletic event?

6 Who scored the winning goal in the 1979 FA Cup Final?

7 What was the nickname of legendary West Indian fast bowler Joel Garner?

8 How many players in an ice hockey team?

9 What sport is Alberto Tomba known for?

10 Who won the Snooker World Championships between 1992 and 1995?

ANSWERS

1. Robert Parish. 2. Manchester United. 3. Amateur. 4. 1975. 5. 110m hurdles. 6. Alan Sunderland. 7. 'Big Bird'. 8. Six. 9. Skiing. 10. Stephen Hendry.

QUIZ 204

• •

1   Where do Wolverhampton Wanderers play football?

2   Who won a gold medal in the 1980 Moscow Olympics for the 1,500m?

3   What sport is Karen Brigg famous for?

4   What is the perfect score in Gymnastics?

5   Why couldn't David Bryant compete in the 1982 Commonwealth Games bowling competition?

6   What Liverpool footballer scored in the final of Euro '96?

7   When did Pete Sampras win his first US Open tennis title?

8   What is boxer James Smith's nickname?

9   Who won the 'Golden Boot' in the 1990 Football World Cup?

10 When the ball in Rugby goes over the touch line, how is the game restarted?

ANSWERS

1. Molineux. 2. Seb Coe. 3. Judo. 4. 10.00. 5. He became professional.
6. Pat Berger. 7. 1990. 8. 'Bone Crusher' Smith. 9. Salvatore Schillachi.
10. Line out.

QUIZ 205

. . . .

1 In what country was Martina Hingis born?

2 Who won the Super Bowl in 1997 for the first time in 29 years?

3 What two players make up the half backs in Rugby Union?

4 Why did Middlesbrough have three points deducted in season 1996–97?

5 In what sport do you play in the 'Silk Cut Challenge Cup'?

6 Whose Arsenal goal scoring record did Ian Wright beat?

7 What sport do you associate Don King with?

8 What sport does Ken Doherty play?

9 In what outdoor pursuit would you do a 'J lean', 'body lean' and 'bell lean'?

10 Dennis Rodman is famous for what sport?

ANSWERS

1. Switzerland. 2. Green Bay Packers. 3. Scrum half and Fly half. 4. They didn't put out a team to play against Blackburn Rovers. 5. Rugby League. 6. Cliff Bastin. 7. Boxing. 8. Snooker. 9. Kayaking. 10. Basketball.

QUIZ 206

. . . .

1 In a Rugby maul is the ball being carried or is it on the floor?

2 Whose rules were adopted in boxing in the 1860s?

3 When was the International Boxing Federation formed?

4 Who was Alex Ferguson's right-hand man at Manchester up until November 1998?

5 Complete the name of the Russian tennis player Yevgeny...?

6 Who is Matthew Pinsent's very successful partner?

7 Who set a World Record for the 200 metres at 19.32 seconds?

8 American Kerri Strug became known for competing in what Olympic sport?

9 Which country failed to turn up to a match against Scotland in 1996?

10 What colour band goes across the jerseys of jockeys racing for Khalid Abdullah?

ANSWERS

1. Being carried. 2. The Marquess of Queensberry. 3. 1983. 4. Brian Kidd.
5. Kafelnikov. 6. Steve Redgrave. 7. Michael Johnson. 8. Gymnastics.
9. Estonia. 10. Pink.

QUIZ 207

1. Who is the only heavyweight boxing champion to have won every professional fight in his career?

2. Who was the much loved vice chairman of Chelsea FC who unfortunately died in a helicopter accident?

3. In 1986 and 1987 which tennis player won both the US and French Opens?

4. Mark Williams won the British Open Snooker Championship, but in what year?

5. What sport does Jan Ullrich compete in?

6. For which Italian football club did Zola and Asprilla play?

7. What Rugby playing country are called the 'Springboks'?

8. Who is the owner of the Williams Formula One racing team?

9. Where is the Dubai Champion Stakes held?

10. How much money do you get for passing 'Go' in Monopoly?

ANSWERS

1. Rocky Marciano. 2. Matthew Harding. 3. Ivan Lendl. 4. Snooker. 5. Cycling.
6. Parma. 7. South Africa. 8. Frank Williams. 9. Rowley Mile at Newmarket.
10. £200.

QUIZ 208

1 What football team won the English Coca Cola Cup in 1997?

2 The Bradford Bulls compete in what sport?

3 What is the final property on a Monopoly board?

4 What sport is Robert Sangster involved in?

5 In which sport would you do an 'Eskimo Roll'?

6 If you were watching in the San Siro, what country would you be in?

7 The BCF are the governing body for which sport?

8 Who was the heavyweight boxing champion for 11 years and 252 days?

9 Who was the manager of the losing team in the 1982 FA Cup Final?

10 In Rugby Union if one of the home countries defeats the other three nations in a season's international matches, what do they achieve?

ANSWERS

1. Leicester. 2. Rugby League. 3. Mayfair. 4. Horse racing. 5. Canoeing.
6. Italy. 7. Cycling (British Cycling Federation). 8. Joe Louis. 9. Terry Venables.
10. The Triple Crown.

QUIZ 209

1 Was Alan Ball in England's World Cup winning football team?

2 If you were playing in the AXA Life Insurance League, what sport would you be playing?

3 What sport are Olga Korbut and Nadia Comaneci famous for?

4 What sport does Herbie Hyde compete in?

5 With which club did Middlesbrough manager Bryan Robson start his playing career?

6 How old was Lester Piggott when he won the Derby on Never Say Die?

7 Who won the British Open Golf Championship in 1997?

8 Carl Foggarty is well known in what sport?

9 What English county side is cricketer Richard Hadlee famous for playing for?

10 Which Italian football team did Ruud Gullit play for?

ANSWERS

1. Yes. 2. Cricket. 3. Gymnastics. 4. Boxing. 5. West Bromwich Albion. 6. 18.
7. Justin Leonard. 8. Super Bike racing. 9. Nottinghamshire. 10. AC Milan.

QUIZ 210

1 Iwan Thomas runs what athletic event for Great Britain?

2 How many players in a Rugby Union team?

3 What job did Christopher Dean do before becoming an ice skater?

4 Who is Gary Neville's footballing brother?

5 When was mountain biking first included in the Olympics?

6 What is the oldest Classic in horse racing?

7 How many players are there in a polo team?

8 Who scored the second goal for England against Scotland in Euro '96?

9 At what weight did Cassius Clay win an Olympic Boxing gold medal in Rome 1960?

10 What fits round your waist and round the rim of the cockpit of a canoe?

ANSWERS

1. 400m. 2. 15 players. 3. Policeman. 4. Phil. 5. 1996. 6. The St Leger.
7. Four. 8. Paul Gascoigne. 9. Light heavyweight. 10. Spray skirt.

QUIZ 211

. . . .

1 What sport do you associate Mike Hailwood with?

2 Joe Frazier won 32 fights in his professional boxing career. How many did he win by knockout?

3 What football team does former prime minister John Major support?

4 What does Hajime mean in Judo?

5 Who scored 501 not out in one innings during 1994?

6 Which snooker player was famously nicknamed 'Hurricane'?

7 How many times did Bernard Hinault win the Tour de France?

8 How many forwards are there in a Rugby Union team?

9 Who did Roy Keane play for before moving to Manchester United?

10 In what sport would you do a 'draw shot', 'drive', 'resting shot' or 'jack trail'?

ANSWERS

1. Motor cycling. 2. 27 by KO. 3. Chelsea. 4. To begin or start the competition. 5. Brian Lara. 6. Alex Higgins. 7. Five times. 8. Eight. 9. Nottingham Forest. 10. Bowls.

QUIZ 212

. . . .

1   In 1997 why couldn't the Grand National be staged on the correct day?

2   What is the name of Sunderland FC's former ground?

3   Boxer Muhammad Ali chose Islam as a faith. What religion did George Foreman opt for?

4   What sport has a governing body with the initials ARA?

5   Who took over from Michael Atherton as England cricket captain?

6   Who won the Five Nations Rugby Tournament in 1997?

7   What country does Leeds United's Lucas Radebe come from?

8   What job does Martin Pipe do in horse racing?

9   John Parrott is famous for what sport?

10 What is the name of the faith healer used by Glenn Hoddle?

ANSWERS

1. Because of an IRA bomb scare. 2. Roker Park. 3. Christianity. 4. Rowing.
5. Alec Stewart. 6. France. 7. South Africa. 8. A trainer. 9. Snooker.
10. Eileen Drewry.

QUIZ 213

1 How many times did Willie Carson become Champion Jockey?

2 If you got a 'turkey' and a 'spare' what leisure activity would you be playing?

3 What colour jersey do the South African Rugby Union team wear?

4 What colour shirts do West Ham United play in?

5 Wigan and St Helen's are top clubs in what sport?

6 How many sixes did Wasim Akram hit in his 257 runs against Zimbabwe in 1996?

7 In what sport are the Thomas Cup and Uber Cup played for?

8 What is the start of a game of Ice Hockey called?

9 What country does footballer David Ginola come from?

10 What country does jockey Steve Cauthen originally come from?

ANSWERS

1. Five. 2. Ten pin bowling. 3. Green with a gold collar. 4. Claret and blue.
5. Rugby League. 6. 12. 7. Badminton. 8. Face-off. 9. France. 10. USA.

QUIZ 214

1. What horse did Bob Champion ride to victory in the 1981 Grand National?

2. How often are the Basketball World Championships held?

3. Did Frank Bruno become the Heavyweight Champion of the World?

4. If you were at a Serie A football match, what country would you be in?

5. Where do the Scottish Rugby Union team play their home internationals?

6. What pop star entertained rain soaked spectators at Wimbledon in 1996?

7. How many points is a 'double top' in darts?

8. Monica Seles won the Australian Open tennis title in 1996. How many times had she already won it?

9. What was the name of the computer that chess player Gary Kasparov played against?

10. In what country was footballer Michael Owen brought up?

ANSWERS

1. Aldaniti. 2. Every four years. 3. Yes. 4. Italy. 5. Murrayfield. 6. Cliff Richard.
7. 40 points. 8. Three times. 9. Deep blue. 10. Wales.

QUIZ 215

. . . .

1 What was the English football team's song for Euro '96?

2 Why couldn't Diane Modahl compete for England in athletics for 19 months?

3 Tennis player Richard Krajicek is from which country?

4 What sport does Pat Eddery compete in?

5 What are the discs used in tiddlywinks called?

6 Jane Sixsmith is famous for playing what sport?

7 What film did Bobby Moore and Pele star in alongside Michael Caine?

8 At what club did Ian Botham finish his cricket career?

9 Who are the 'Super Sonics' in Basketball?

10 What is the name of Serena Williams's tennis playing sister?

ANSWERS

1. 'Football's Coming Home/Three Lions'. 2. She was wrongly accused of taking drugs. 3. Holland. 4. Horse racing. 5. Winks. 6. Hockey. 7. Escape to Victory. 8. Durham. 9. Seattle. 10. Venus Williams.

QUIZ 216

. . . .

1 What team does Shaquille O'Neal play for in the NBA?

2 What football team won 'the double' in 1986?

3 John Lowe is famous for what sport?

4 'Googlies', 'flippers' and 'wrong 'uns' can be found in which sport?

5 For what country did Gavin and Scott Hastings both play Rugby Union?

6 Who are England's joint leading goal scorers of all time?

7 In fencing there are three types of sword. What are they?

8 The game 'Fives' originates from which public school?

9 Who came second in the Grand National on Garrison Savannah in 1991?

10 In the game of nim, what small items are most commonly removed?

ANSWERS

1. LA Lakers. 2. Liverpool. 3. Darts. 4. Cricket. 5. Scotland. 6. Bobby Charlton and Gary Lineker. 7. Foil, épée and sabre. 8. Eton. 9. Mark Pitman. 10. Matchsticks.

QUIZ 217

1 In what sport would you do a Harai goshi?

2 Boxer Michael Spinks only lost once in his reign as heavyweight champion. Who beat him?

3 What pop star is footballer Jamie Redknapp married to?

4 What country does former tennis player Ilie Nastase come from?

5 What is the horse piece in chess called?

6 What is the player called who puts the ball into the scrum in Rugby Union?

7 What is the highest score you can check out on in darts?

8 What job did England player Rory Underwood do outside of Rugby?

9 How many Classics are there in the flat season of horse racing?

10 Who were the 1988 men's Olympic Hockey Champions?

ANSWERS

1. Judo. 2. Mike Tyson. 3. Louise. 4. Romania. 5. Knight. 6. Scrum half. 7. 170. 8. RAF pilot officer. 9. Five. 10. Great Britain.

QUIZ 218

. . . .

1 What sport do Rodber and Ubogu play?

2 What country does Dwight Yorke come from?

3 In what sport might you play on the ATP Tour?

4 What sport is basically a combination of cross country running and map reading?

5 Neil Ardley plays for what Premiership football team?

6 How many players are there in a Rugby League team?

7 What sport is Matt Biondi known for?

8 What are the two main forms of competition weight lifting?

9 Cricketer Viv Richards, during his career, moved from Somerset to which county side?

10 How many points do you get for a 'bullseye' in darts?

ANSWERS

1. Rugby Union. 2. Tobago, West Indies. 3. Tennis. 4. Orienteering.
5. Wimbledon FC. 6. 13. 7. Swimming. 8. Snatch and Clean, and Jerk.
9. Glamorgan. 10. 50 points.

QUIZ 219

. . . .

1 Who won the 1988 Rugby League World Cup?

2 When sailing what is the right hand side of a boat called when one is looking forward?

3 What races make up the US Triple Crown in horse racing?

4 When was the Biathlon introduced as an Olympic sport?

5 What football team play at the Sixfields Stadium?

6 Where do the English Rugby Union team play their home internationals?

7 Except for in America, how many players are there in a softball team?

8 What is the name of the American goalkeeper who plays for Leicester City?

9 What Open Championship did Arantxa Sanchez Vicario win in 1989 and 1994?

10 How tall is Antiguan fast bowler Curtly Ambrose?

ANSWERS

1. Australia. 2. Starboard. 3. Kentucky Derby, Preakness Stakes and Belmont Stakes. 4. 1960. 5. Northampton Town. 6. Twickenham. 7. Nine. 8. Kasey Keller. 9. French. 10. Six feet seven inches.

QUIZ 220

. . . .

1 What is the women's equivalent to the Davis Cup in tennis?

2 Where do Ipswich Town play football?

3 Before Newcastle what Rugby team did Rob Andrew play for?

4 What country did racing driver Juan Manuel Fangio come from?

5 Who did Slaven Bilic play for before Everton?

6 In 1985 how many horse racing Classics did Steve Cauthen win?

7 In what sport would you play for the Stanley Cup?

8 What is footballer Sol Campbell's full Christian name?

9 At what public school was the game of squash developed?

10 What sport did Trevor Berbick and Tim Witherspoon compete in?

ANSWERS

1. Federation Cup. 2. Portman Road. 3. Wasps. 4. Argentina. 5. West Ham.
6. Four. 7. Ice hockey. 8. Sulzeer. 9. Harrow School. 10. Boxing.

QUIZ 221

• •

1 In what year did Stan Smith win the Wimbledon singles title?

2 What is the real name of Hawaiian born Sumo wrestler 'Akebono'?

3 What country does goalkeeper Mark Bosnich come from?

4 What is the name of England's best loved boxer turned pantomime star?

5 In which sport would you use a foil?

6 What football team play at Roots Hall?

7 Who became the first woman to complete the Grand National course in 1982?

8 How many people compete in the annual University Boat Race?

9 In snooker, how many consecutive pots must be made when scoring a maximum break?

10 What football team were the runners up in both the major English Cups in 1993?

ANSWERS

1. 1972. 2. Chad Rowan. 3. Australian. 4. Frank Bruno. 5. Fencing.
6. Southend United. 7. Geraldine Rees. 8. 18 including coxes. 9. 39.
10. Sheffield Wednesday.

QUIZ 222

• •

1 Who holed the first televised 'hole in one'?

2 What country does footballer Phillipe Albert come from?

3 In what year did Liz McColgan win the London Marathon?

4 Who rode 'Nijinsky' to a Derby win in 1970?

5 Frank Bruno lost when he defended his world title against Mike Tyson in March 1996. What belt did Tyson win?

6 Did Sterling Moss ever win the Formula 1 World Championship?

7 From 501 what is the least number of darts that can be used to check out?

8 What country does Rugby player Joel Stransky come from?

9 Leicester City brought centre back Matt Elliott from what lower league side?

10 What is the back of a boat called?

ANSWERS

1. Tony Jacklin. 2. Belgium. 3. 1996. 4. Lester Piggott. 5. WBC. 6. No. 7. Nine.
8. South Africa. 9. Oxford United. 10. Stern.

QUIZ 223

• •

1 Which two male swimmers hold the record of seven medals in a single Olympic Games?

2 What manager signed Mark Wright for Liverpool in 1991?

3 What is Mike Tyson's boxing nickname?

4 Which sport is Joe Davis known for?

5 What colour jerseys do the New Zealand Rugby Union team wear?

6 What is Tino Asprilla's full Christian name?

7 What swimming race would competitors start in the water rather than diving in?

8 In what outdoor activity would you find classes called 'C1', 'C2', 'K1' and 'K2'?

9 What England cricket captain got in trouble for allegedly rubbing dirt and soil on a ball?

10 Where do Walsall play football?

ANSWERS

1. Mark Spitz and Matt Biondi. 2. Graeme Souness. 3. 'Iron Mike'. 4. Snooker.
5. Black. 6. Faustino. 7. Back stroke. 8. Canoeing. 9. Michael Atherton.
10. The Bescot Stadium.

QUIZ 224

1. David Beckham is famous for scoring a goal from the halfway line. Who was the goalkeeper?

2. Who was the captain of the English Rugby Union team in 1998?

3. What athletic event did Sally Gunnell win in 1993, setting a new world record?

4. In 1998 what Welshman played cricket for England?

5. What part of a cycling race would you expect Jean Paul Van Poppel to come into his element?

6. Complete the name of the boxer: Thomas ... Hearns.

7. What is the nickname of Huddersfield Town FC?

8. What is the least distance from the ditch that a 'long jack' can be in bowls?

9. Who won the Wimbledon women's doubles title with Steffi Graf in 1988?

10. What country is West Ham footballer Eyal Berkovic from?

ANSWERS

1. Neil Sullivan. 2. Lawrence Dallaglio. 3. 400-metre hurdles. 4. Robert Croft.
5. A sprint. 6. Thomas 'The Hitman' Hearns. 7. 'The Terriers'. 8. Six feet.
9. Gabriela Sabatini. 10. Israel. 6. Horse racing.

QUIZ 225

1 How many players are there in a netball team?

2 What sport did Katarina Witt perform in?

3 In what sport would you use a pommel horse?

4 Jeremy Guscott presents the TV show The Gladiators, but what sport is he famous for playing?

5 What football team play at The Dell?

6 When would you wear the yellow jersey on the Tour de France?

7 Who won an Olympic sprint gold medal in 1988 but had it taken away for taking performance enhancing drugs?

8 What is aikido?

9 Who are nicknamed 'The Bluebirds' in football?

10 What county cricket team does Darren Gough play for?

ANSWERS

1. Seven. 2. Figure skating. 3. Gymnastics. 4. Rugby Union. 5. Southampton.
6. When leading the race. 7. Ben Johnson. 8. A Japanese system of self-defence that is similar to judo, but includes blows from the hands and feet.
9. Cardiff City. 10. Yorkshire.

QUIZ 226

1 Sheikh Mohammed is involved in what sport?

2 What country does famous goalkeeper Bruce Grobbelaar come from?

3 Who is the well known snooker player from Malta?

4 What kind of bowler is Pakistan's Saqlain Mushtaq?

5 Which dog won both the English and Irish Derbies in 1998?

6 What country do Brann Bergen play football in?

7 In March 1996 who did the England Rugby team beat 18–9?

8 In which city was Johann Cruyff born?

9 Who won the first Benson & Hedges Cup, in 1972?

10 Who are 'The Eagles' in football?

ANSWERS

1. Horse racing. 2. Zimbabwe. 3. Tony Drago. 4. Spinner. 5. Tom's the Best.
6. Norway. 7. Scotland. 8. Amsterdam. 9. Leicestershire. 10. Crystal Palace.

QUIZ 227

1 Which cricketer has taken the most test wickets of all time?

2 Which Italian football team did Jimmy Greaves play for?

3 What event does athlete Nick Buckfield compete in?

4 Where would you play the game Baccarat?

5 Who did Henry Cooper fight on 18 June 1963?

6 What football team does Patrick Viera play for?

7 In what sport would you compete for the America's Cup?

8 When was curling first introduced as a proper Olympic event?

9 What football club is Alan Sugar the chairman of?

10 What sport do you associate Jack Rowell with?

ANSWERS

1. Kapil Dev. 2. AC Milan. 3. Pole vault. 4. In a casino. 5. Mohammed Ali.
6. Arsenal. 7. Yachting. 8. 1998 (Nagano). 9. Tottenham Hotspur. 10. Rugby Union.

QUIZ 228

• •

1 How many World Opens did squash player Jansher Khan win?

2 What shape is a rugby ball?

3 With which Formula 1 racing team did Nigel Mansell win the World Championship?

4 In what year did Kieran Perkins break the 400, 800 and 1,500 metres swimming world records?

5 Who took over from Michael Atherton as England cricket captain?

6 What is the racquet used in lacrosse called?

7 What team did American football legend Dan Marino play for between 1983 and 1997?

8 Steve Bull is a hero at which football club?

9 What activity is the descent of a steep slope, or vertical drop, by a rope secured above?

10 Juan Antonio Samaranch is the president of what committee?

ANSWERS

1. Eight. 2. Oval. 3. Williams Renault. 4. 1994. 5. Alec Stewart. 6. A crosse. 7. Miami Dolphins. 8. Wolverhampton Wanderers. 9. Abseiling. 10. IOC (International Olympic Committee).

QUIZ 229

1 Which English football team did Brian Roy play for?

2 Elvis Stojko competed for Canada in what sport?

3 What cricket player became a bishop in the Church of England?

4 In what sport might you win a penalty corner?

5 Stan Flashman was the chairman of what football club?

6 If you were fishing would you catch a black bass in salt water or fresh water?

7 How high off the ground is the crossbar on Rugby goalposts?

8 How high is the front wall in a squash court?

9 Kelly Slater is famous for what sport?

10 For which distance did swimmer Alexander Popov hold the world record?

ANSWERS

1. Nottingham Forest. 2. Figure skating. 3. David Shepherd. 4. Hockey. 5. Barnet. 6. Fresh water. 7. Three metres. 8. 15 feet high. 9. Surfing. 10. 50 metres.

QUIZ 230

• •

1. Which jockey overcame cancer to win the 1981 Grand National?

2. Wet flies, dry flies, nymphs and streamer flies are all used in what sport?

3. In what game would you use a shot called a 'boast'?

4. In tennis, what score is called 'deuce'?

5. What is skeet shooting?

6. How many dice do you use in a game of Backgammon?

7. What famous football city is seven miles away from Aintree racecourse?

8. What sport is Prince Charles famous for playing?

9. Where is horse racing's William Hill Sprint Championship held?

10. What country won the men's doubles table tennis title at the 1988 and 1992 Olympics?

ANSWERS

1. Bob Champion. 2. Fly fishing. 3. Squash. 4. Forty all. 5. A form of clay-pigeon shooting (in which targets are hurled from two traps at different speeds and angles). 6. Two. 7. Liverpool. 8. Polo. 9. York. 10. China.

QUIZ 231

. . . .

1 Where do Norwich City play their home games?

2 How many cards are there in a pack?

3 If you were watching the Green Bay Packers what sport would you be watching?

4 How long is a full length snooker table?

5 Which is the only club outside of Britain that Ian Rush has played for?

6 What team did Manchester United buy Henning Berg from?

7 'Blue Gill' and 'Crappies' are found in what hobby?

8 What colour caps do jockeys riding for H. J. Joel wear?

9 Which sport takes place in a velodrome?

10 Ronnie O'Sullivan is famous for which sport?

ANSWERS

1. Carrow Road. 2. 52. 3. American football. 4. 12 feet. 5. Juventus.
6. Blackburn Rovers. 7. Fishing (they are fish). 8. Red. 9. Cycling. 10. Snooker.

QUIZ 232

. . . .

1 In which sport would you find, Fenders, Mothers, Sheets and Reefs?

2 Who is the only man to have played both Cricket and Rugby Union for England at ful international level?

3 Which member of the Royal Family has won an Olympic Medal?

4 Which player traditionally throws the ball in at a Rugby Union line out?

5 In snooker, if there are two reds left and I clear the table gaining the maximum points available, how many points have I scored?

6 Who are the only team from outside the USA to win Baseball's World Series?

7 Who won the 1997 Grand National Steeplechase?

8 Who won the 1997 Coca Cola Cup?

9 With which team did Nigel Mansell make his Formula One debut?

10 Who was captain of the victorious England Cricket team for the 1997 Sharjah one day tournament?

ANSWERS

1. Sailing. 2. Alistair Hignall. 3. The Princess Royal (Princess Anne).
4. The Hooker. 5. 43. 6. The Toronto Blue Jays. 7. Lord Galeen.
8. Leicester City. 9. Lotus. 10. Adam Hollioake.

QUIZ 233

• •

1. At which sport does Jane Sixsmith represent England?

2. Which former England Centre led Newcastle to the Division One title in 1998 as their Director of Rugby?

3. What is the minimum number of darts required to complete a leg from 501?

4. If I score 'Was-a-ri' in Judo, how many points have I scored?

5. Name the two Williams drivers for the 1998 Formula One season.

6. For which rally team did Colin McRae drive in 1997 & 1998?

7. Is 'The Oaks' a race for colts or fillies?

8. Who was the longest-serving England cricket captain?

9. Name Arsenal's highest ever scorer.

10. In the 1970s Brian Jacks rose to national fame due to the 'Superstars' television programme, but in which sport did he actually compete for Great Britain at international level?

ANSWERS

1. Hockey. 2. Rob Andrew. 3. Nine. 4. Half. 5. Heinz Harold Frentzen and Jacques Villeneuve. 6. Subaru. 7. Fillies. 8. Mike Atherton. 9. Ian Wright. 10. Judo.

QUIZ 234

• •

1 For which Formula One team did Nigel Mansell win the World Drivers' Championship?

2 For which County Cricket team did Brian Lara play in the 1997 & 1998 seasons?

3 Who were Rugby Union Division One champions in the 1996/97 season?

4 Apart from Manchester United and Arsenal, up until 1999, which was the only other team to have won the Premier League?

5 Who is the only British Olympian to have won Gold Medals in three consecutive Olympic Games?

6 Name Denver's American football team.

7 Which British swimmer won the 100m Breaststroke Gold Medal in the 1980 Olympic Games?

8 With which club did Bobby Moore end his professional playing career?

9 By which name was wrestler Shirley Crabtree better known?

10 Who was the first British boxer in the 20th century to win a World Heavyweight title?

ANSWERS

1. Williams. 2. Warwickshire. 3. Wasps. 4. Blackburn Rovers. 5. Steven Redgrave. 6. Broncos. 7. Duncan Goodhew. 8. Fulham. 9. Big Daddy. 10. Lennox Lewis.

QUIZ 235

• •

1 Where do Surrey County Cricket Club play the majority of their home games?

2 Name Phoenix's NBA Basketball team?

3 Which football team was Eric Morecambe renowned for supporting?

4 How many players are there in a Polo team?

5 Who was England's top scorer in the 1992 Olympic Hockey tournament?

6 Who scored a hat-trick against England in the 1992 European Championships?

7 Name Houston's American football team.

8 Which British cyclist who won a gold medal at the 1992 Olympic Games on a radical graphite and carbon-fibre bike?

9 Who won the 1998 Rugby League Challenge Cup?

10 In Rugby Union what can you do inside your own 22, but not outside, unless it's a penalty?

ANSWERS

1. The Oval. 2. The Suns. 3. Luton Town. 4. Four. 5. Sean Kerley. 6. Marco Van Basten. 7. Oilers. 8. Chris Boardman. 9. Sheffield Eagles. 10. Kick the ball, 'out on the full',

QUIZ 236

. . . .

1 Name Queens Park Rangers' home ground.

2 Name Pittsburgh's American football team.

3 What do Skoal Bandit, Zakspeed and Lotus have in common?

4 Name the British adventurer who led the successful Thrust II supersonic land speed record attempt.

5 What sport do Poole Pirates take part in?

6 What nationality was Greg Rusedski at birth?

7 Which sport played in the southern hemisphere is a cross between Rugby, American football and Gaelic football, with teams such as the Essendon Bombers and Footscray Bulldogs?

8 Where do the 'Broncos' English Rugby League team come from?

9 In Cricket, a batsman may only score a maximum of 30 leg byes in any one innings. True or false?

10 Who was the first person to break the four-minute mile?

ANSWERS

1. Loftus Road. 2. The Steelers. 3. They are all ex-Formula One teams.
4. Richard Noble. 5. Speedway. 6. Canadian. 7. Australian Rules Football.
8. London. 9. False. 10. Roger Banister.

QUIZ 237

1 Colin Jackson is famous for which athletics event?

2 If I was playing Stapleford rules, what sport would I be playing?

3 In which county is Headingley cricket ground?

4 Which snooker player is nicknamed 'The Whirlwind'?

5 Which snooker player gained the nickname, 'The Hurricane'?

6 Who managed Leeds United to a UEFA Cup place in the 1997/98 season?

7 Name Atlanta's Baseball team.

8 Which jump jockey holds the record for the most winners in a season?

9 Which British squash player finally ousted Jansher Khan as world number one in 1998?

10 In Cricket, and excluding the wicket keeper, which fielding position is usually nearest the bat?

ANSWERS

1. 110m Hurdles. 2. Golf. 3. Yorkshire. 4. Jimmy White. 5. Alex Higgins.
6. George Graham. 7. The Braves. 8. Tony McCoy. 9. Peter Nichol. 10. Silly point.

QUIZ 238

. . . .

1   If I was sitting on the 'Strip', watching the 'Christmas Tree' and revving my 'Rail', what sport would I be taking part in?

2   Which football team play at Maine Road?

3   Who captained Essex County Cricket team during the 1994 season?

4   In American Football how many points are awarded for a 'Safety'?

5   What are the three disciplines in a Triathlon?

6   If Stoke City were playing a home derby match, who would they be playing?

7   Who won the 1994 women's Rugby World Cup?

8   In which month is the Kentucky Derby run?

9   Who provided the engines for the 1998 McLaren Formula One team?

10 What do the initials MCC stand for?

ANSWERS

1. Drag Racing. 2. Manchester City. 3. Graham Gooch. 4. Two. 5. Swimming, Cycling and Running. 6. Port Vale. 7. England. 8. May. 9. Mercedes Benz. 10. Marylebone Cricket Club.

QUIZ 239

1 Which county cricket team has its home at Old Trafford?

2 In 1994, which country hosted the Winter Olympics?

3 By which name is Rugby Union's William Henry Hare better known?

4 If I were to 'Serve, Dig, Spike or Set', what sport would I be playing?

5 In equestrianism, which rider with the first name Nick, won the World Cup in 1995?

6 Alison Fisher is one of the leading female exponents of which sport?

7 In which country did Pele finish his professional playing career?

8 What does 'PB' against a runner's time indicate?

9 Who, before Lynford Christie, last won an Olympic 100m gold medal for Britain?

10 What was ex-England hooker Brian Moore's occupation when not on the Rugby pitch?

ANSWERS

1. Lancashire. 2. Norway. 3. Dusty. 4. Volleyball. 5. Nick Skelton. 6. Snooker. 7. USA. 8. Personal Best. 9. Alan Wells. 10. Solicitor.

QUIZ 240

. . . .

1 Which football club is generally accepted as the oldest in England?

2 Peter Shilton played his 1000th league game with which club?

3 Kendo is the ancient Japanese art of what?

4 A cricket umpire holds both arms straight up above his head to indicate what?

5 How often is the US Masters golf tournament held?

6 Which county did former England cricket captain Tony Greig also lead?

7 By joining, which country will turn the Five Nations Rugby Union tournament into the 'Six Nations'?

8 For what feat will the gymnast Nadia Comaneci always be remembered?

9 What is the name of New Orleans American football team?

10 In the Tour de France what does the green jersey signify?

ANSWERS

1. Notts County. 2. Leyton Orient. 3. Sword fighting. 4. Six runs.
5. Every year. 6. Sussex. 7. Italy. 8. The first perfect 10 score in a major competition.

QUIZ 241

. . . .

1 What was American footballer William Perry's nickname?

2 David Bedford is associated with which sport?

3 Where was the 1986 Football World Cup held?

4 What is the nickname of Wigan's Rugby League team?

5 Whilst playing which sport did Prince Charles break his arm?

6 Which Pam was Martina Navratilova's doubles partner?

7 What sport do the Boston Red Socks play?

8 Who was the first person to have been in charge of both England and Australia's football teams?

9 Which city hosted the 1972 Olympic Games?

10 Who was the first overseas manager to win the FA Cup?

ANSWERS

1. The Fridge. 2. Athletics. 3. Mexico. 4. Warriors. 5. Polo. 6. Shriver.
7. Baseball. 8. Terry Venables. 9. Munich. 10. Ruud Gullit.

QUIZ 242

. . . .

1 Name Minnesota's American Football team.

2 Who sponsors the traditional curtain raiser to Wimbledon, at Queens Club?

3 How many players are there in a Ryder Cup team?

4 How many hulls does a catamaran have?

5 With which sport do you associate Tony Jarrett?

6 Which sport did Nigel Mansell move to after leaving Formula One?

7 Who sponsored Jaguar's successful challenge at Le Mans?

8 Name the odd one out: Pike, Chub, Roach, Pouting.

9 What nationality is tennis player Gabriella Sabatini?

10 Which football team plays its home games at The Valley?

ANSWERS

1. Vikings. 2. Stella Artois. 3. Twelve. 4. Two. 5. Athletics (110m Hurdles).
6. Indy Car Racing. 7. Silk Cut. 8. Pouting is a sea fish. 9. Argentinian.
10. Charlton Athletic.

QUIZ 243

. . . .

1 In which city is the annual World Professional Snooker Championship held?

2 Who captained the Scottish Rugby Union team during it's 1990 Grand Slam victory?

3 Which race was won 14 times by Mike Hailwood?

4 Which Chinese game involves 144 tiles divided into six suits?

5 In which sport do you refer to the pitch as a Gridiron?

6 What is the maximum score possible in one game of Ten Pin Bowling?

7 In which sport would you compete for the Air Canada Silver Broom?

8 Which sport features banderillas, veronicas, muletas and picadors?

9 Which is larger: the United States or British golf ball?

10 How many hits are allowed on one side of the net in Volleyball?

ANSWERS

1. Sheffield. 2. David Sole. 3. Isle of Man TT. 4. Mah Jong. 5. American Football. 6. 300. 7. Curling. 8. Bull Fighting. 9. US. 10. Three.

QUIZ 244

• •

1 Who is the only man to have won World Titles at both motor cycle and car racing?

2 Which sporting figure re-enacted Hannibal's crossing of the Alps for charity?

3 Which football club formerly played their home games at The Baseball Ground?

4 With which team did Damon Hill begin his Formula One career?

5 Who was the, 'Crafty Cockney', winner of the World Professional Darts Championship in 1980?

6 Which US baseball star married Marilyn Monroe?

7 Which sporting star was kidnapped in 1983, never to be seen again?

8 Which team always leads the Olympic parade?

9 What is New Zealand's Rugby League team known as?

10 In which sport are the balls made of crystallate?

ANSWERS

1. John Surtees. 2. Ian Botham. 3. Derby County. 4. Williams. 5. Eric Bristow.
6. Joe DiMaggio. 7. Shergar. 8. Greece. 9. The Kiwis. 10. Snooker.

QUIZ 245

. . . .

1   From which country does Tae Kwon Do originate?

2   Name the four competition swimming strokes?

3   How many players are there in a Water Polo team?

4   Who was the youngest man ever to win a singles title at Wimbledon?

5   What is the height of a Badminton net: 4ft 9ins, 5ft 1in, 5ft 4ins or 5ft 9ins?

6   In TT motorcycle racing, what does TT stand for?

7   Name Detroit's American football team?

8   In Rugby Union, how many players are linked together in a scrum?

9   Who was the English goalkeeper who could not stop the 'Hand of God'?

10 In show jumping how many faults are awarded for a refusal?

ANSWERS

QUIZ 246

• •

1 In Luge Tobogganing do competitors travel feet or head first?

2 Name Boston's NBA Basketball team?

3 What is the aim of a Puissance show jumping event?

4 Who is the youngest man ever to play football for England at full international level?

5 In cricket what was originally in Dorset Square, then where Marylebone station currently stands and is now in St John's Wood?

6 In Rounders, what is awarded if the bowler delivers three 'no-balls'?

7 At which sporting event would you have a 'Barrel Man', hold a 'Cinch', have a 'Hang-up' and sit in a 'Shute box'?

8 At which racetrack is the 2000 Guineas run?

9 Name the variant of Lawn Bowls predominantly played in the North of England?

10 What is the official distance for a Marathon?

ANSWERS

1. Feet first. 2. Celtics. 3. To jump higher than anyone else. 4. Michael Owen. 5. Lord's Cricket Ground. 6. Half-Rounder. 7. Rodeo. 8. Newmarket. 9. Crown Green Bowls. 10. 26miles 385yds (42.2km).

QUIZ 247

● ●

1   How many players are there on an, 'Aussie Rules' football team?

2   How long is an American football pitch?

3   On what surface is the game of, 'Bandy', played?

4   Which is usually smaller, a Rugby League ball or a Rugby Union ball?

5   Which sport would I be taking part in if I were competing in, The Scottish Six Days Trial?

6   Starting in Paris, where does the world famous rally finish?

7   Where do the, 'Mets', Baseball team come from?

8   Over which course is the St Leger run?

9   Which Arsenal Goalkeeper missed the 1973 FA Cup Final, due to a broken leg, and later became a commentator first on the BBC, then ITV?

10 Wayne Gretzky having scored more than 2000 points in under 850 games, is regarded as one of the greatest exponents of which sport?

ANSWERS

1. Eighteen. 2. 100yds. 3. Ice. 4. Rugby League Ball. 5. Motorcycle Trials Riding. 6. Daker. 7. New York. 8. Doncaster. 9. Bob Wilson. 10. Ice Hockey.

QUIZ 248

• •

1 In Lawn Bowls what is the target ball known as?

2 In which country did the sport of Petanque originate?

3 Which equestrian sport is broken down into, Trotting and Pacing events, where the drivers sit on lightweight carts and the horses are not permitted to gallop?

4 Where is the King George VI Chase run?

5 How many players are there in an outdoor Handball team?

6 Who was the bowler that was hit for six sixes by Sir Garfield Sobers in one over?

7 What is the diameter of a netball net: 15ins, 16ins, 17ins or 18ins?

8 In which sport would you use a half-butt, a spider and an extended spider?

9 Which football team plays its home games at Upton Park?

10 At the Olympics, in which sport would you compete in the Trap and Skeet events?

ANSWERS

1. The Jack. 2. France. 3. Harness Racing. 4. Kempton Park. 5. Eleven.
6. Derek Nash. 7. 15ins. 8. Snooker. 9. West Ham United. 10. Clay Target shooting.

QUIZ 249

• •

1 Over which course is the Whitbread Gold Cup run?

2 What is the second most expensive property in the British version of Monopoly?

3 Who won the British Open Golf Tournament in 1985?

4 In Rugby, who feeds the ball in to the scrum?

5 For which sport is Joe Montana famous?

6 Which football team play at, 'The Dell'?

7 Where do the Seahawks American Football team come from?

8 Over which course is the Grand National run?

9 What sport do the Sheffield Eagles play?

10 How many players are there in a Netball team?

ANSWERS

1. Sandown Park. 2. Park Lane. 3. Sandy Lyle. 4. Scrum Half. 5. American Football. 6. Southampton. 7. Seattle. 8. Aintree. 9. Rugby League. 10. Seven.

QUIZ 250

. . . .

1 Which three football teams were promoted to the Premiership in 1997 only to be relegated the following year?

2 What is the technical term for making a sail smaller, whilst it's still attached to the mast?

3 On what course is golf's U.S. Masters played?

4 Name Cincinnati's American football team?

5 Which sport do the London Towers play?

6 In cricket, what is the maximum length of a Test Match?

7 Which sport was played at the Olympic Games in 1900, where the French collected all six Gold medals, but was never again an Olympic sport?

8 Jill Hammersley and Carl Prean are known for playing which sport?

9 What two skills are combined in the sport of Orienteering?

10 Name three events in a heptathlon?

ANSWERS

1. Barnsley, Bolton and Crystal Palace. 2. Reefing. 3. Augusta National.
4. Bengals. 5. Basketball. 6. Five days. 7. Croquet. 8. Table Tennis.
9. Running & Map Reading. 10. 100m hurdles, Shot put, High jump, 200 m, Long jump, Javelin and 800 m.

QUIZ 251

1. In American football, which player scores, 'the point after'?

2. Which Italian footballer missed the deciding penalty to give Brazil victory in the 1994 World Cup Finals?

3. Which game is faster, Rugby Fives or Eton Fives?

4. In Tennis, name the four Grand Slam events?

5. In Squash, which ball is slowest, a red dot, a blue dot or a yellow dot?

6. Name the famous snooker and billiards playing brothers who dominated the games in the middle of this century?

7. In which sport would you use, a Do, a Shinai, a Kote and a Hakama?

8. How old was Mike Tyson when he won his first World Heavyweight title?

9. Which football team plays its home matches at, 'The Hawthorns'?

10. Which form of skiing was the first to be organised competitively?

ANSWERS

1. The Kicker. 2. Roberto Baggio. 3. Rugby Fives. 4. Wimbledon and the Australian, French and US Opens. 5. Yellow dot. 6. Joe and Fred Davis. 7. Kendo. 8. Twenty. 9. West Bromwich Albion. 10. Ski jumping.

QUIZ 252

. . . .

1   The 'Yankees' baseball team comes from which city?

2   In Rugby Union who competes for the Calcutta Cup?

3   The Hennessy Gold Cup is run over which race course?

4   From where does the sport of Pelota originate?

5   What other sport is regularly played at Lord's Cricket Ground?

6   Who was the number two driver for Ferrari's Formula One team in the 1997 & 1998 seasons?

7   What calibre rifles are used in the Biathlon, Nordic Skiing event?

8   In a four man Bobsleigh, where does the, 'brakeman' sit?

9   In championship darts from what score do competitors start each leg?

10 In Judo if the Referee says, 'Hajime!', what should you do?

ANSWERS

1 New York. 2. Scotland and England. 3. Newbury. 4. The Basque region of Spain. 5. Real Tennis. 6. Eddie Irvine. 7. .22. 8. At the rear. 9. 501. 10. Start fighting.

QUIZ 253

• •

1 In Golf, what is the term used for two under par at a hole?

2 Where did the 1992 summer Olympics take place?

3 After retiring from international competition, which British shot putter made his name by winning international, 'Strong Man', competitions?

4 Which Scottish footballer is the only player to have scored 100 goals in both the English and Scottish football leagues?

5 How many players are there in a Baseball team?

6 With which sport do you associate Carl Fogarty?

7 What six-a-side sport starts with a 'face-off'?

8 In which sport would you compete for the Davis Cup?

9 Which sport was ruled by the Hambledon Club, from Halfpenny Down in the 1700s?

10 Which country do the, 'Socceroos', represent?

ANSWERS

1. Eagle. 2. Barcelona. 3. Geoff Capes. 4. Kenny Dalglish. 5. Nine. 6. Motor Cycling. 7. Ice Hockey. 8. Tennis. 9. Cricket. 10. Australia.

QUIZ 254

. . . .

1 Edgbaston is the home ground of which County cricket team?

2 Name Sheffield Wednesday's football ground?

3 Which former striker and Gladiators host was accused of match fixing?

4 What happened to Colombian defender Andres Escobar when he returned home after scoring an own goal to put his team out of the 1994 World Cup?

5 How long is a squash racket's handle: 27ins, 29ins, 30ins or 32ins?

6 With which sport do you associate Canadians, Gasper & Benoit?

7 True or false in the 1900 Olympic Games, live birds were used in the pigeon shooting contest?

8 From which country does Muki boxing come?

9 If you were a Juryo entering a Basho, which sport would you be taking part in?

10 In total how many players are permitted in an Ice Hockey team?

ANSWERS

1. Warwickshire. 2. Hillsborough. 3. John Fashanu. 4. He was shot.
5. 27ins. 6. Luge Tobogganing. 7. True. 8. India. 9. Sumo Wrestling.
10. 20.

QUIZ 255

. . . .

1 Which British swimmer won a breaststroke gold medal in the 1980 Olympics?

2 With which sport do you associate Mary Peters?

3 What do, Chris Waddle, Stuart Pearce and Paul Ince have in common?

4 Name Washington's American football team?

5 Which Scottish defender suffered the indignity of Paul Gascoigne lobbing the ball over his head to then chip it into the goal, during Euro 96?

6 With which sport do you associate David Bryant?

7 Which British sports personality of the year gained notoriety for swearing while collecting the trophy from the Princess Royal?

8 With which athletic event do you associate Sergei Bubka?

9 Which England football manager was controversially portrayed as a turnip by the tabloid press?

10 Great Britain have won the Olympic Hockey gold medal three times. True or false?

ANSWERS

1. Duncan Goodhew. 2. Heptathlon. 3. They have all missed penalties in World Cup penalty shootouts where England have been eliminated. 4. Redskins. 5. Colin Hendry. 6. Bowls. 7. Daley Thompson. 8. Pole Vault. 9. Graham Taylor. 10. False.

QUIZ 256

. . . .

1 What was Nigel Benn's fighting nickname?

2 What music usually accompanies Chris Eubank as he enters the boxing arena?

3 Name Green Bay's American football team?

4 With which sport do you associate Peekaboo Street?

5 Which England goalkeeper had a premature end to his career when he injured an eye in a car accident?

6 In the 1997/98 season who did Mohammed Al Fayed appoint as Director of Football at Fulham?

7 Which Formula One driver also owned an airline?

8 Which former Tottenham player captained Germany during the 1998 World Cup?

9 Which horse is buried at the Aintree winning post?

10 Who won the 1998 European Cup Winners Cup?

ANSWERS

1. The Dark Destroyer. 2. 'Simply The Best' (Tina Turner). 3. Packers.
4. Ski-ing. 5. Gordon Banks. 6. Kevin Keegan. 7. Nikki Lauda. 8. Jürgen
Klinsman. 9. Red Rum. 10. Chelsea.

QUIZ 257

● ●

1 With which sport do you associate Michael Doohan?

2 In American football how many yards do you have to gain, in order to achieve a 'First down'?

3 With which sport do you associate the Searle brothers?

4 Who scored for England in the 1966 World Cup final, apart from Geoff Hurst?

5 Judo, in Japanese, means, 'the Gentle way'. True or False?

6 With which sport do you associate Jesper Parnevik?

7 Name Warrington's Rugby League team?

8 What nationality is three-day eventer, Mark Todd?

9 With which sport do you associate Armand de la Cuevas?

10 Which sport is famous for being played at the 'Guards Club'?

ANSWERS

1. Motor Cycling. 2. Ten. 3. Rowing. 4. Martin Peters. 5. True. 6. Golf.
7. Wolves. 8. New Zealand. 9. Cycling. 10. Polo.

QUIZ 258

. . . .

1 What nationality the is golfer Tom Lehman?

2 In which sport would you compete for the Curtis Cup?

3 What is the term used to describe a female horse less than four years old?

4 At which weight did boxer Chris Eubank make a comeback in 1998?

5 Who captained Glamorgan County Cricket team during their championship winning season, 1997?

6 With which sport do you associate John Francome?

7 Name San Diego's American football team?

8 What number did Paul Gascoigne usually wear for England?

9 How many points is a free throw in basketball worth if scored?

10 In Judo, apart from throwing your partner or pinning him to the ground, how do you score points?

ANSWERS

1. American. 2. Golf (Women's). 3. Filly. 4. Cruiserweight. 5. Matthew Maynard. 6. Horse Racing. 7. Chargers. 8. Eight. 9. One. 10. By gaining a submission.

QUIZ 259

• •

1 True or false, the Tour de France always takes place exclusively within France?

2 What always goes to the FA Cup final but never appears?

3 In the mid 1980's F1 team, Zakspeed were sponsored by cigarette manufacturer, West. What did the team paint on the side of the cars to beat tobacco advertising bans?

4 Which football team's official nickname is, 'The Lillywhites'?

5 Which day of the week is 'Ladies day' at Royal Ascot?

6 In which sport might you use the controversial 'Great Big Bertha', or 'Ti Bubble 2'?

7 What nationality is the tennis star Martina Hingis?

8 If I was throwing my ball with a 'chistera', against the wall of the 'cancha', what sport would I be playing?

9 What sport do the Washington Bullets play?

10 In which year was the America's Cup won for the first time by a boat not from the United States?

ANSWERS

1. False. 2. The losing team's ribbons. 3. East. 4. Tottenham Hotspur.
5. Thursday. 6. Golf. 7. Swiss. 8. Pelota. 9. Basketball. 10. 1983.

QUIZ 260

- -

1. During cycling time trials how many cyclists are on the track at any one time?

2. How many times has Tom Watson won the US Masters Championship?

3. Which country will become the 10th Cricketing Test Nation?

4. Which football team plays their home matches at the Stadium of Light?

5. Robin Cousins and John Curry are the only British men to have won Olympic Men's Figure Skating gold medals. True or False?

6. In Ten Pin Bowling what term describes knocking ten pins down with two balls?

7. Who was the last Briton to win a singles title at Wimbledon?

8. What nationality is former Newcastle striker Faustuno Asprilla?

9. Which cricketer had the nickname 'Beefy'?

10. Who is Great Britain's delegate on the International Olympic Committee?

ANSWERS

1. One. 2. Twice. 3. Bangladesh. 4. Sunderland. 5. True. 6. Spare.
7. Virginia Wade. 8. Colombian. 9. Ian Botham. 10. The Princess Royal.

QUIZ 261

. . . .

1 Which football team plays their home games at 'The New Den'?

2 What is the accepted length of a field hockey pitch?

3 What do the initials TCCB stand for?

4 Which sporting archive was established at Cooperstown, New York State, in 1934?

5 With which sport do you associate Michael Whitaker?

6 Which sport is descended from Byerly Turk, Darley Arabian and Godolphin Arabian?

7 What did Belgian Joseph Merlin invent in 1760, which was improved on 100 years later by American Everett Plimpton, which today is the basis for several leisure sports?

8 How many disciplines are there in a Women's international gymnastics event?

9 In Olympic athletics, how long is a steeplechase?

10 This sport first became popular in the 13th Century. Its first purpose-built playing area was opened in Southampton in 1299. Its rules were unified in the 19th century, although different variations still prevail in the North of England. What is it?

ANSWERS

1. Millwall. 2. 100 yards (91.5m). 3. Test and County Cricket Board.
4. Baseball's Hall of Fame. 5. Show Jumping. 6. Horse Racing. 7. The Rollerskate. 8. Four. 9. 3000m. 10. Lawn Bowls.

QUIZ 262

. . . .

1 What makes Sculls different to conventional rowing?

2 In 1990 Hale Irwin won the US Open Golf Championship. What record did he set in doing this?

3 What nationality is Tennis star Anna Kournikova?

4 With which sport do you associate Dennis Rodman?

5 Who set the world 100m record of 9.84 seconds at the 1996 Olympics?

6 Which World Cup hero was knighted in the 1998 Queens Birthday honours list?

7 Name New York's AFC American Football team?

8 In Martial Arts such as Judo and Karate, what name is given to the ritual exercises that develop technique, and physical and mental strength?

9 In horse racing, by what name is a male horse less than four years old referred to?

10 Where did the sport of Polo originate?

ANSWERS

1. In Sculls, each oarsman has two oars, in Rowing they have one.
2. Oldest player to win the tournament. 3. Russian. 4. Basketball.
5. Donovan Bailey. 6. Sir Geoff Hurst. 7. The Jets. 8. Kata. 9. A Colt.
10. Persia (Iran).

QUIZ 263

· ·

1. What is the premier UK Rally event?

2. Which British Racing driver came second in the Monte Carlo Rally in 1952, second at Le Mans in 1956, as well as winning 36 Grand Prix?

3. Which sport was invented by American William G. Morgan, a physical training instructor from Holyoke, Massachusetts, involves 2 teams of 6 players, held its first world championship in 1949, and has accepted as an Olympic sport in 1964?

4. In which sport would you compete for the Federation Cup?

5. What sport do the Denver Nuggets play?

6. In m.p.h., how fast is a Knot?

7. In which 1982 event did Mark Thatcher get lost?

8. Which British Formula One driver was nicknamed 'The Shunt'?

9. Which sports does the FINA organisation preside over?

10. In which sport do you aim to get a ringer but sometimes get a leaner whilst standing in the pitching box?

ANSWERS

1. The Lombard RAC Rally. 2. Stirling Moss. 3. Volleyball. 4. Tennis.
5. Basketball. 6. 1.15mph. 7. The Paris-Dakar Rally. 8. James Hunt.
9. Swimming, Waterpolo and Diving. 10. Horseshoe Pitching.

QUIZ 264

• •

1   In Baseball which player wears the most protective clothing?

2   What did Frenchman, Baron Pierre de Courbetin, do in the late 19th Century that would provide a whole new focus for the sporting world?

3   Which Rugby Union club plays its home games at Welford Road?

4   With which sport, other than football, do you associate Jack Charlton?

5   What is the term used in Golf to describe two over par at a hole?

6   Which sport holds its main British events at Santa Pod?

7   Which American event, first run in 1911, requires competitors to cover 200 laps of a 2.5 mile circuit?

8   Which sport does the ITTF govern?

9   True or false. In Netball, only 2 players on each team are allowed to score goals?

10 Which sport did the All England Croquet Club take responsibility for in 1874, asking the Marylebone Cricket Club to write the rules?

ANSWERS

1. The Catcher. 2. Resurrected the Olympic Games. 3. Leicester. 4. Fishing.
5. Double Bogey. 6. Drag Racing. 7. Indianapolis 500. 8. Table Tennis.
9. True. 10. Lawn Tennis.

QUIZ 265

1 Which sport do the Hawthorn Hawks play?

2 In Rugby Union, how far must the ball travel from the kick off?

3 In 1921 the Fédération Equestre Internationale laid down the rules for which sport?

4 In which year was the first 'Modern' Olympic Games held in Athens?

5 How long is the wire on a hammer in Athletics; 0.9m, 12m, 15m or 19m?

6 What was introduced into America in 1644 by Colonel Richard Nicholls, Commander of the English Forces?

7 What nationality is sprinter Frankie Fredericks?

8 Who took over as Chairman of Newcastle United after his son resigned amid controversy?

9 What does the word 'Karate' mean in Japanese?

10 With which sport do you associate Jonah Barrington and Susan Devoy?

ANSWERS

1. Australian Rules Football. 2. 10 yards. 3. Dressage. 4. 1896. 5. 1.2m.
6. Horse Racing (Flat Racing). 7. Namibian. 8. Sir John Hall. 9. Empty Hand.
10. Squash.

QUIZ 266

1 In Snooker, how many points is the blue ball worth?

2 Name Tampa Bay's American football team?

3 Which County Cricket team does Andrew Flintoff play for?

4 Which football club has the nickname the 'Eagles'?

5 With which sport do you associate Kirk Stevens?

6 What is the nationality of cricketer David Boon?

7 Who are the only father and son ever to both win the Formula One Drivers World Championship?

8 Which sport competes for the Bledisloe Cup?

9 What nationality is racing driver, Thierry Boutson?

10 With which sport do you associate David Broom?

ANSWERS

1. Five. 2. Buccaneers 3. Lancashire. 4. Crystal Palace. 5. Snooker.
6. Australian. 7. Graham and Damon Hill. 8. Rugby Union. 9. Belgian.
10. Show Jumping.

QUIZ 267

1 Where were the 1968 Olympics held?

2 With which club side did Will Carling finish his playing career?

3 In which sport would you use a 'Trace, a 'Beaked Barb' and a 'Waggler'?

4 Who was Italy's manager/coach during France '98?

5 With which sport do you associate Kieran Fallon?

6 Up to 1998, Will Carling was the last England Captain to win a Grand Slam. True or False?

7 In Offshore Power Boat racing, the task of piloting the boat is usually shared between two people. If one steers what does the other do?

8 Who manufactured England's 1998 World Cup strip?

9 With which sport do you associate Nancy Kerrigan?

10 In Italia '90, which England player scored the winner that knocked out Belgium?

ANSWERS

1. Mexico. 2. Harlequins. 3. Fishing. 4. Cesare Maldini. 5. Horse Racing.
6. True. 7. Controls the throttles. 8. UMBRO. 9. Ice Skating. 10. David Platt

QUIZ 268

1 Which female British Athlete won the New York marathon in 1991?

2 Which county does Sally Gunnell come from?

3 After completing his studies, what career did Will Carling, embark on?

4 Which British athlete was cleared of drugs charges on appeal in March 1996?

5 What's the nationality of racing driver Nelson Piquet?

6 Which snooker ball is worth six points?

7 Which sport do the Worthing Bears play?

8 For what county did BBC cricket commentator, Jonathon Agnew, play most of his cricket?

9 In racing, what does the abbreviation SP stand for?

10 The Bulls versus the Rhinos is a local derby in which county?

ANSWERS

1. Liz McColgan. 2. Essex. 3. An Army Officer. 4. Diane Modahl.
5. Brazil. 6. Pink. 7. Basketball. 8. Leicestershire. 9. Starting Price.
10. Yorkshire (Rugby League).

QUIZ 269

• •

1 Name New England's American Football Team?

2 How many players are there on a 'Bandy' team?

3 How long is a 'Period' in an NBA basketball match?

4 The husband of Princess Caroline of Monaco, Stefano Cariraghi, died in 1990 taking part in which sport?

5 What nationality is footballer Davor Suker?

6 Which four-man event was accepted into the Olympic Games when it was held at Chamonix, France, in 1924?

7 Which sport, governed by the ICF, was introduced into the Calgary Olympics as a demonstration sport in 1988?

8 If you were playing 14:1 continuous play rules, what game would you be taking part in?

9 In '3 Position' target shooting events, what are the 3 positions?

10 Which sport held its first professional world championships in 1978, now held annually, at the Lakeside Club in Camberley?

ANSWERS

1. Patriots 2. Eleven. 3. Twelve minutes. 4. Power Boat Racing.
5. Croatian. 6. Bobsleigh. 7. Curling. 8. Pool. 9. Prone, kneeling and standing.
10. Darts.

QUIZ 270

• •

1 Name Baltimore's Major League baseball team?

2 At which football club's ground would you find the Stretford End?

3 Which sport do the Barcelona Dragons play?

4 Who or what are Goldie and Isis?

5 Which Rugby Union club does British Lion and Army officer, Tim Rodber, play for?

6 What is the total width of a Badminton court. 18ft, 20ft, 22ft or 26ft?

7 Who won an incredible six World Snooker Championships in the 1980s?

8 How many players are there on a Basketball court at any one time?

9 Name the three Olympic athletic field events that are still men-only?

10 What is the minimum weight of a tennis ball; 55g, 55.9g, 56.3g or 56.7g?

ANSWERS

1. Orioles. 2. Manchester United. 3. American Football. 4. Oxford and Cambridge Number Two Crews. 5. Northampton. 6. 20 ft. 7. Steve Davis. 8. Ten. 9. Triple Jump, Hammer and Pole Vault. 10. 56.7g.

QUIZ 271

. . . .

1   In American football, how many points are awarded for a field goal?

2   In which sport are you not allowed to refer to females as women, but always as ladies?

3   What are a jockey's Silks?

4   Whilst Cardiff Arms Park was being renovated, where did the Welsh Rugby Union team play their home games?

5   Where is the British Grand Prix currently held?

6   Which football club did Brian Robson manage in the 1997/98 football season?

7   True or false. Tim Henman and Greg Rusedski have the same birthday?

8   Name Britain's top woman Boxer who became the first woman to be granted a Licence by the British Boxing Board of Control?

9   Who were the main sponsors of the Jordan Formula One team during the 1998 season?

10 Which professional sport does the WPBSA preside over?

ANSWERS

1. Three.   2. Show Jumping.   3. His coloured shirt.   4. Wembley.   5. Silverstone.
6. Middlesborough. 7. True.   8. Jane Couch.   9. Benson and Hedges.
10. Billiards and Snooker.

QUIZ 272

. . . .

1 Which winter sport does ex-England Cricket Captain David Gower regularly take part in at St Moritz?

2 Which football team plays its home games at Goodison Park?

3 With which sport do you associate Brian Johnston?

4 Name the American football team based in Dallas?

5 In Formula One, what change in the rules led to the running of two separate Grand Prix Championships in the mid 1980's?

6 In Water Polo, what happens to a player who commits three personal faults in one match?

7 In which year was Canoeing introduced into the Olympic Games; 1920, 1924, 1932 or 1936?

8 Footballer Ian Rush was granted a Soccer scholarship, by a US university. True or false?

9 What did swimmer Captain Matthew Webb achieve in 1875?

10 How many balls are there on a Billiards Table?

ANSWERS

1. Tobogganing (Skeleton). 2. Everton 3. Cricket. 4. The Cowboys 5. The banning of Turbo Chargers. 6. Banned for the rest of the game. 7. 1936.. 8. False. 9. First person to swim the English Channel. 10. Three

QUIZ 273

• •

1 What is the diameter of a Basketball hoop; 30cm, 40cm, 45cm or 50cm?

2 How long is an Olympic-sized swimming pool?

3 Which ski's are narrower - Cross Country (Nordic) or Downhill?

4 What material is the tip of a Snooker Cue made from?

5 Who won the Men's Singles at Wimbledon in 1997?

6 With which sport do you associate Iwan Thomas?

7 In international swimming events, how warm must the water be; 20°C, 22°C, 24°C or 26°C?

8 Which team scored in injury time in all three of its group matches in France '98?

9 With which sport do you associate James Wattana?

10 Which football team play their home games at the Nou Camp Stadium?

ANSWERS

1. 45cm. 2. 50m. 3. Downhill. 4. Leather. 5. Pete Sampras. 6. Athletics (400m). 7. 24°C. 8. Austria. 9. Snooker. 10. Barcelona.

QUIZ 274

• •

1   In Athletics, how high is a Steeplechase Hurdle;
    2ft 6ins, 2ft 9ins, 3ft 0ins or 3ft 6ins?

2   In Rugby Union, which players form part of the
    back row on each side of the scrum?

3   Which County Cricket team plays the majority of
    their home matches at Chester-le-Street?

4   Who kept goal for Scotland in the 1998 World
    Cup finals, after Andy Goram returned home amid
    allegations concerning his personal life?

5   Which wood is a cricket bat traditionally made
    from?

6   Which sport do the Richmond Tigers play?

7   Which football team play their home games at
    Craven Cottage?

8   How many players are there in a Lacrosse team?

9   For which British Touring Car Championship Team
    did TV presenter Mike Smith drive?

10 With which team did Nigel Mansell win the
    Formula One World Driver's Championships?

ANSWERS

1. 3ft 0ins. 2. Flanker (Wing Forward). 3. Durham 4. Jim Leighton
5. Willow. 6. Australian Rules Football. 7. Fulham. 8. Ten. 9. BMW.
10. Williams.

QUIZ 275

. . . .

1 When England and Australia play for the Ashes, the contents of the urn are reputed to be what?

2 How many crew are there in a Tornado Sailing Boat?

3 In Judo, which is the higher grade, White Belt, Yellow Belt or Blue Belt?

4 Which sport usually uses the larger pitch, Rugby League or Rugby Union?

5 What is the maximum number of players permitted in a Rounders Team?

6 Who won the 1996/97 Carling Premiership?

7 Which of Horse racing's classics is the oldest?

8 Who was John Mcenroe's normal doubles partner?

9 Which one of these golf courses is the odd one out: Birkdale, Troon, Gleneagles, Carnoustie?

10 In what sport might you catch a crab?

ANSWERS

1. Ashes of a burnt cricket bail 2. Two. 3. Blue Belt. 4. Rugby Union.
5. Nine 6. Manchester United. 7. St. Leger. 8. Peter Fleming. 9. Birkdale - others are in Scotland. 10. Rowing.

QUIZ 276

. . . .

1 'Lutz' is a term used in which sport?

2 How many squares are there on a traditional Snakes and Ladders board?

3 'The Curtis Cup' is awarded for which sport?

4 In ice hockey, how many players from each side are allowed on the ice at any one time?

5 In rowing, what is the name of the Oxford University reserve team?

6 In what sport did Alberto Tomba compete for Italy at Olympics and World Championships?

7 In horse racing betting circles, how much is a bet of a 'monkey' worth?

8 Which Scottish Rugby Union Captain also plays American football?

9 In ten pin bowling, what is a 'spare'?

10 What is the value in points of a pink ball in snooker?

ANSWERS

1. Skating. 2. 100. 3. Golf. 4. 6. 5. Isis. 6. Skiing. 7. £500. 8. Gavin Hastings.
9. Two consecutive bowls which, combined, knock ten pins down. 10. Six.

QUIZ 277

- -

1. In Monopoly, what colour is the set 'Trafalgar Square, Fleet Street and Strand'?

2. 'The Derby' is held at which racecourse?

3. How many home bases are there in baseball?

4. 'Eskimo Roll' is a term used in which sport?

5. What does 'TT' stand for in the Isle of Man motorcycle races?

6. Which game was invented in 1931 by the architect Alfred Butts?

7. Who was the first woman tennis player to win one million dollars in prize money?

8. In which sport was Ty Cobb an outstanding player?

9. Which batsman scored six 6s in one over in a match between Nottinghamshire and Glamorgan in 1968?

10. After whom was the first football World Cup trophy named?

ANSWERS

1. Red. 2. Epsom. 3. Five. 4. Canoeing. 5. 'Tourist Trophy'. 6. Scrabble. 7. Chris Evert. 8. Baseball. 9. Gary Sobers. 10. Jules Rimet.

QUIZ 278

1. What is the diameter in metres of the circle from which a discus is thrown?
2. What is the name of a powered hang-glider?
3. How many players comprise a World Cup Squad?
4. How many points are scored when the goal-kicker converts a try in Rugby Union?
5. How many goals did Geoff Hurst score in the 1966 World Cup Final?
6. What is the value of the outer central ring on a dartboard?
7. What is the term for the main group of cyclists in a race?
8. Which football manager said: 'Some people think football is a matter of life and death. I can assure them it is much more serious than that'?
9. Which is the oldest of the English classic horse races?
10. How many players are there in an indoor handball team?

ANSWERS

1. 2.5. 2. A microlight. 3. 22. 4. 2. 5. 3. 6. 25. 7. The peloton. 8. Bill Shankly. 9. The St Leger. 10. Seven.

QUIZ 279

1 On which English race course is the Derby run?

2 How many Gold medals did Michelle Smith win for Eire, in the 1996 Olympic Games?

3 Who captained the South African cricket team in 1998?

4 Which team did Chelsea beat to win the 1998 European Cup Winners Cup Final?

5 By what name are Bradford's Rugby league team known?

6 Which darts player was nicknamed 'the Crafty Cockney'?

7 In which Olympic swimming races do competitors start in the water?

8 What is the American equivalent of the card game pontoon?

9 What Chinese game has a name that means 'the sparrows'?

10 Which boxer was world heavyweight champion between 1919 and 1926?

ANSWERS

1. Epsom. 2. Three. 3. Hansie Cronje. 4. Stuttgart. 5. The Bulls. 6. Eric Bristow. 7. Backstroke. 8. Blackjack. 9. Mahjong. 10. Jack Dempsey.

QUIZ 280

1. Who was BBC TV personality of the year in 1996?

2. What incident in a German tennis tournament, meant that Monica Seles was injured and out of tennis for over a year?

3. Which European city hosts the games of the American football team known as 'Galaxy'?

4. Up until 1998 who sponsored the World Professional Snooker Championship?

5. In the Euro '96 match between Germany and England, what was the score after extra time?

6. What is the usual term for a golf course by the sea?

7. In which city is the Waca cricket ground?

8. What was the name of the US high jumper who originated the technique of jumping over the bar headfirst and backwards?

9. What sport do the Chicago Bulls play?

10. What nationality was the figure skater Sonja Henie?

ANSWERS

1. Jonathan Edwards. 2. She was stabbed, on court, by a fan of Steffi Graf.
3. Frankfurt. 4. Embassy. 5. 1-1. 6. A golf links. 7. Perth, Australia. 8. Dick Fosbury. 9. Basketball. 10. Norwegian.

QUIZ 281

1 One of the most successful skiers of the 1990s was Alberto Tomba, what nationality is he?

2 Which sport do Birchfield Harriers take part in?

3 Who won the Golden Boot in the 1986 World Cup finals?

4 Who sponsored the 1998 Rugby League Challenge Cup Final?

5 Who won the 1997 British Touring Car Championship?

6 What is the first name of the jockey Dunwoody?

7 In which sport would the term 'Shortstop' be used?

8 How many times did Jackie Steward win the Formula 1 World Championship?

9 In boxing, who drew up a set of rules in 1867?

10 What colour jacket is awarded to the winner of the US Masters golf tournament?

ANSWERS

1. Italian. 2. Athletics. 3. Gary Lineker. 4. Silk Cut. 5. Alain Menu. 6. Richard.
7. Baseball. 8. 3. 9. The Marquess of Queensberry (John Sholto Douglas).
10. Green.

QUIZ 282

· ·

1 Which two football teams play each other in the Edinburgh derby match?

2 What sport do the Manchester Giants play?

3 For which Formula One team did James Hunt win the World Drivers' Championship?

4 What was the score in the 1998 FA Cup final, when Arsenal defeated Newcastle to take the League and Cup double?

5 Which heavyweight boxer is nicknamed, 'The Real Deal'?

6 In 1998 which County Cricket team did Robin Smith captain?

7 With which county is the family name Cowdrey synonymous?

8 In which year did Virginia Wade win the Wimbledon singles title?

9 Who captained the England Rugby Union team during their 1998 tour of the southern hemisphere?

10 What nationality is the athlete Haile Gebresilassie?

ANSWERS

1. Heart of Midlothian and Hibernian 2. Basketball 3. McLaren 4. 2-0
5. Evander Holyfield 6. Hampshire. 7. Kent 8. 1997 9. Matt Dawson
10. Ethiopian

QUIZ 283

1 What sport do the Cardiff Devils play?

2 Ice Dance champions Torvill and Dean are associated most with which piece of music?

3 The 'Buccaneers' American football team come from which US city?

4 Name West Bromwich Albion's football ground?

5 Name the five disciplines in the modern pentathlon?

6 Name Utah's NBA Basketball team?

7 Which of the following is not a coarse fish, Chub, Dace, Grayling, Carp?

8 With which sport do you associate David Campese?

9 Who scored England's opening goal in the 1998 World Cup?

10 Who sponsored Rugby League's Super League in 1998?

ANSWERS

1 Ice Hockey 2. Bolero by Ravel 3 Tampa Bay 4. The Hawthorns 5. Fencing, Swimming, Shooting, Running and Horse Riding 6. The Jazz 7. Grayling 8. Rugby Union 9. Alan Shearer 10. JJB

QUIZ 284

. . . .

1 How high is the net on a tennis court: 2ft 6ins, 3ft or 3ft 4ins?

2 How old was Stephen Hendry when he became Snooker's world number one?

3 Name the three events in equestrian three-day eventing?

4 In which European country was the sport of Handball invented?

5 By what name was the USA's Olympic Basketball team known in the 1996 Olympic Games?

6 In the 1970s which brand of cigarettes became synonymous with the Lotus Formula One team.

7 Which County Cricket team plays the majority of their home games at the Oval?

8 With which sport do you associate Robert Fox?

9 Which football club plays its home games at the Riverside?

10 Who provided the engines for William's F1 team, during their triumphant 1996 season?

ANSWERS

1. 3ft 2. 20 3. Dressage, Cross Country and Show Jumping 4. Germany
5. The Dream Team 6. JPS 7. Surrey. 8. Modern Pentathlon
9. Middlesborough 10. Renault

QUIZ 285

• •

1   How wide is a discus throwing circle: 2.5m, 2.7m or 3.1m?

2   Which sport was the subject of the Popplewell Report in 1985?

3   What do the initials BBBC stand for?

4   In 1990 the horse Mr Frisk set a record time in which major race?

5   In which major sporting championship does the winner receive a, 'Green Jacket'?

6   With which sport do you associate John Parrott?

7   Who won the 1997 FA Cup?

8   How many American footballers per team are allowed on the field at any one time?

9   From what material are boules made?

10 In athletics what is the maximum permitted amount of wind assistance that can be received for a record to stand?

ANSWERS

1. 2.5m 2. Football 3. British Boxing Board of Control 4. The Grand National
5. US Masters (Golf) 6. Snooker. 7. Chelsea 8. 11 9. Steel
10. 2m per second

QUIZ 286

• •

1 What is the highest possible 'Out' shot in darts?

2 Name the home city for 'The 49ers', American Football team.

3 How many players are there in a Gaelic Football team?

4 How old was Brian Clough when he finished his playing career; 29, 31, 34 or 38?

5 Where is the Leander Rowing Club based?

6 Whom did Tony Blair appoint as Sports Minister in 1997?

7 In Polo, how long does a 'Chuka' last?

8 Which sport do the West Coast Eagles play?

9 How many men form a line out in Rugby League?

10 In Euro 96 how many teams did England beat without the use of a penalty shoot-out?

ANSWERS

1. 170 2. San Francisco 3. 15 4. 29 5. Henley-on-Thames 6. Tony Banks
7. Seven minutes 8. Australian Rules Football 9. None (you don't have line outs in Rugby League) 10. Two

QUIZ 287

1 In Golf, what is the term for one under par at a hole?

2 What sport do the Scottish Claymores play?

3 If you were at Goodison Park or Anfield which city would you be in?

4 Who won the 1998 Rugby Union Women's World Cup?

5 For which Italian side did 'Gazza', play?

6 Which football team play their home games at Ewood Park?

7 Which Brazilian won the Formula One World Drivers Championships in 1981, 1983 and 1987?

8 How high is a table tennis net; 4ins, 5ins, 6ins, or 7ins?

9 What sport do the Sacramento Kings play?

10 How long is a quarter in Water Polo?

ANSWERS

1 Birdie 2. American Football 3. Liverpool 4. New Zealand 5. Lazio
6. Blackburn Rovers 7. Nelson Piquet 8. Six inches 9. Basketball
10. Seven minutes

QUIZ 288

• •

1 Bob Nudd was World Champion at which sport?

2 Who was the first man to win the Embassy World Snooker Championship twice?

3 What was Mohammed Ali's original name?

4 Mick the Miller was a champion at which sport?

5 Which controversial British athlete reputedly tripped Mary Decker in the 1984 Olympics?

6 What is the height of the biggest competition ski-jump hill?

7 Which city hosts the Grand National?

8 How old was Jonah Lomu when he played in his first Rugby World Cup?

9 How many rowers are in an International Dragon Boat team?

10 In judo, which belt follows the Yellow Belt?

ANSWERS

1. Angling 2. Steve Davis 3. Cassius Clay 4. Greyhound Racing 5. Zola Budd
6. 90 metres 7. Liverpool 8. 20 years old 9. 26 rowers 10. Orange

QUIZ 289

•••••••••••••••••••••••••••••••

1 Who was the first man to defeat Frank Bruno in a world title fight?

2 In which sport are players awarded Brownlow Medals?

3 Who was man-of-the-match in the 1998 England v South Africa test at Headingley?

4 Which tennis player has won more women's singles titles than any other, and in 1984 set the longest winning streak of 74 victories?

5 For which Club did England star Graeme Le Saux play during the 1997/98 season?

6 Where were the 1994 Winter Olympic Games held?

7 Which darts player has won the World Masters Championship five times, the World Professional Championship five times and the World Cup Singles four times?

8 Which Rugby League player has won 33 winner or runner-up medals in his career?

9 Which rowing regatta has been an annual event since 1839?

10 How many balls are used in a game of pool?

ANSWERS

1. Tim Witherspoon 2. Australian Rules Football 3. Mark Butcher
4. Martina Navratilova 5. Chelsea 6. Lillehammer, Norway 7. Eric Bristow
8. Shaun Edwards 9. Henley 10. 16, including white

QUIZ 290

1 June Croft is associated with which sport?

2 How many lanes are there in an Olympic-sized swimming pool?

3 Which stick and ball game uses the largest pitch?

4 By what name is footballer Edson Arantes do Nascimento better known?

5 Which is the first 'Classic' of the English Horse racing season?

6 What is the maximum height difference (between start and finish lines) in any Nordic Cross Country Ski event?

7 Which Argentinean did David Beckham 'kick out at' in St Etienne during the 1998 World Cup?

8 The now notorious Will Carling, captained England a world record 42 times. In that time how many games did England win?

9 In what sport would you be competing if you had to perform the 'Volte', 'Piroutte' and 'Serpentine'?

10 Anthony Hembrick, USA, was the Boxing Gold Medal favourite in Seoul, 1988. Why did he not win any medals?

ANSWERS

1 Swimming 2. Eight 3. Polo 4. Pelé 5. The 1000 Guineas 6. 250 m (273 yds) 7. Diego Simone 8. 31 games 9. Equestrianism (dressage) 10. He missed the team bus to stadium and missed the bout

QUIZ 291

- -

1. How many times did the San Francisco 49ers win the Super Bowl in the 1980s?

2. Which race course is the home of the 'St Leger'?

3. In what country is the NHL the national Ice Hockey League?

4. What game is Nigel Short famous for?

5. From where did Newcastle United buy England International Robert Lee?

6. In all Alpine Skiing races, skiers race between gates consisting of two coloured flags. What are the two colours?

7. How many metres is a furlong?

8. The world's prestigious Rugby Seven's tournament was first hosted in 1976. In which country?

9. In which sport did Sean Kerly compete for Great Britain in the 1984 and 1988 Olympics?

10. How many press-ups did Charles Servizio complete during 24 hours in California, April 1993?

ANSWERS

1. Three times 2. Doncaster 3. Canada 4. Chess 5. Charlton Athletic FC
6. Red and blue 7. 201 metres 8. Hong Kong 9. Hockey 10. 46,001
(forty six thousand and one)

QUIZ 292

. . . .

1 Michael Chang is the youngest tennis player to win which Grand Slam event?

2 In gymnastics men use the horizontal bar. What is the female equivalent?

3 With which sport do you associate Greg LeMand?

4 Where was the 1970 Football World Cup held?

5 What sport and leisure activity is the film Kingpin about?

6 How many times have Jayne Torvill and Christopher Dean won the British Ice Dance Championships?

7 White City in London was famous for athletics and which other track sport?

8 Philippe Sella appeared over 100 times for France between 1982 and 1994. How many times did he appear?

9 Boxer, Mike Tyson was jailed for what offence in the early 1990s?

10 Name the first, male British gymnast to win a medal at the World Championships in 1993.

ANSWERS

1. French Open 2. The asymmetric bars 3. Cycling 4. Mexico 5. Ten Pin Bowling 6. Seven 7. Greyhound Racing 8. 101 9. Rape 10. Neil Thomas

QUIZ 293

. . . .

1 How many minutes is a game of rugby?

2 In what sport do you compete for the Lonsdale Belt?

3 From what football club did Tottenham Hotspur sign Darren Anderton?

4 With which sport is John McCririck involved?

5 'Traversing' is a term from what sport and leisure activity?

6 Which British skater jumped 19' 1" in an axel jump in November 1983?

7 In a 1990 Gallup Poll, which famous race horse achieved higher public recognition than Norman Lamont, the Chancellor?

8 Which Rugby League player broke the transfer record in 1992 when transferring from Widnes to Wigan for £440,000?

9 In which sport would you be taking part if you were 'Luffing', 'Gybing' and 'Bearing Away'?

10 In Rugby Union what number does the hooker have?

ANSWERS

1. 80 minutes 2. Boxing 3. Portsmouth 4. Horse racing 5. Skiing 6. Robin Cousins 7. Desert Orchid 84% (Norman Lamont 77%) 8. Martin Offiah 9. Yachting 10. Two

QUIZ 294

. . . .

1 Who won the 1980 Snooker World title?

2 How many times have France won the football World Cup?

3 If a fielder stops a cricket ball with a cap, helmet or jumper, how many runs does he concede?

4 What is the shape of an Australian Rules football pitch?

5 Which Scottish football club did Danish International Brian Laudrup play for?

6 How many times did Nelson Piquet win the Formula 1 World Championships?

7 What piece in chess can only be moved diagonally?

8 Who said 'You cannot be serious'?

9 Who are 'The Cottagers' in football?

10 William Webb Ellis is responsible for giving us which sport?

ANSWERS

1. Cliff Thorburn. 2. Once (1998). 3. Five runs. 4. An oval. 5. Glasgow Rangers. 6. Three. 12 Bishop. 8. John McEnroe. 9. Fulham. 10. Rugby.

QUIZ 295

. . . .

1 What country does chess player Gary Kasparov come from?

2 Dr James Naismith is responsible for creating the modern version of what sport?

3 Who did Australia beat in the final of the 1991 Rugby Union World Cup?

4 Which football team has the nickname 'The Villains'?

5 In which sport did Lloyd Honeyghan formerly compete?

6 What football team play at Maine Road?

7 What country are the 'All Black' Rugby team from?

8 From which country do ex-Tottenham footballers Ossie Ardiles and Ricky Villa come?

9 Who rode West Tip to Grand National victory in 1986?

10 On what island did bungee jumping originate?

ANSWERS

1. Russia. 2. Basketball. 13. England. 4. Aston Villa. 5. Boxing. 6. Manchester City. 7. New Zealand. 8. Argentina. 9. Richard Dunwoody. 10. Pentecost Island.

QUIZ 296

. . . .

1 In what year did Nick Faldo win both the US Masters and the Open Championship?

2 Which county cricket side has three swords on their team badge?

3 Who was the famous owner of the horse 'Indian Skimmer'?

4 Which two nations competed in the final of the 1995 Rugby Union World Cup Final?

5 What colour is the eight ball in a game of pool?

6 Who is the oldest ever US Open Golf Champion?

7 What do the initials MCC stand for?

8 Mario Andretti won the Formula 1 World Championship in 1977. True or false?

9 Where do Newcastle United FC play their home games?

10 The Baseball World Series is out of the best of how many games?

ANSWERS

1. 1990. 2. Essex. 3. Sheikh Mohammed. 4. South Africa and New Zealand.
5. Black. 6. Hale Irwin. 7. Marylebone Cricket Club. 8. False (1978).
9. St James Park. 10. Seven games.

QUIZ 297

• •

1. Celebrity cook Delia Smith is on the board of what football club?

2. What player receives the Cy Young award in American Baseball every year?

3. In which sport is Wayne Gretzky a superstar?

4. How many goals did Gary Lineker score in the 1986 football World Cup Finals?

5. For what hobby would you need maggots, worms and crab?

6. Who became the youngest golfer to win the US Masters, in 1997?

7. Name the four tennis tournaments that make up the Grand Slam?

8. Where do Watford Football Club play their home fixtures?

9. Pirmin Zurbriggen is a World Cup winner in which sport?

10. How many points is an 'H' worth in Scrabble?

ANSWERS

1. Norwich City. 2. The outstanding pitcher in the major leagues. 3. Ice hockey. 4. Six. 5. Fishing (bait). 6. Tiger Woods. 7. Wimbledon, Australian Open, French Open and US Open. 8. Vicarage Road. 9. Downhill Skiing. 10. Four points.

QUIZ 298

. . . .

1 What sport did Jocky Wilson play?

2 What is the maximum break in Snooker?

3 For which club did Paul Ince play in Italy?

4 What is the name of Jacques Villeneuve's famous father?

5 What is the maximum length of a Rugby Union field of play?

6 What are the officials called in a game of cricket?

7 What is the name of the Chicago basketball team?

8 If you were watching an 'Old Firm' derby, in which city would you be?

9 For what type of dancing do you dress up like cowboys and do moves like the 'camel walk' and 'the stomp'?

10 What is the nickname of Northampton Town FC?

ANSWERS

1. Darts. 2. 147. 3. Inter Milan. 4. Gilles Villeneuve. 5. 100 metres. 6. Umpires. 7. Chicago Bulls. 8. Glasgow. 9. Line dancing. 10. 'The Cobblers'.